Reducing Restraints in He e: Practice and Policy ectives

Safeguarding Adults Team
Jubilee Centre
Darley Street
Bolton   BL1 3DX

Note

Health and social care practice and knowledge are constantly changing and developing as new research and treatments, changes in procedures, drugs and equipment become available.

The authors, editor and publishers have, as far as is possible, taken care to confirm that the information complies with the latest standards of practice and legislation.

Reducing Restraints in Health and Social Care: Practice and Policy Perspectives

Edited by
Rhidian Hughes

QUAY
BOOKS

A division of MA Healthcare Ltd

Quay Books Division, MA Healthcare Ltd, St Jude's Church, Dulwich Road, London
SE24 0PB

British Library Cataloguing-in-Publication Data
A catalogue record is available for this book

ISBN-10: 1 85642 376 X
ISBN-13: 978 1 85642 376 2

Printed by CLE, St Ives, Huntingdon, Cambridgeshire

Contents

Foreword

Lord Carlile of Berriew QC, FKC, LlB
A Master of the Bench of The Hon Soc of Gray's Inn

This book is topical and timely. Nearly two years before writing this foreword I chaired an Inquiry for the Howard League for Penal Reform into the use of restraints on children in custody. The Howard League report included local authority secure children's homes, thereby overlapping the contents of this book. Following prolonged debate on and around the issues described in our Report, the Government commissioned and responded to a report on the issue. The report and response failed to make the really necessary challenge to the fundamentals of the problems identified. There is no doubt that there will be continuing focus, until there is legislation to remove or severely curtail the use of restraints in custody and comparable settings.

That these are important matters should be self-evident. The unnecessary use of violence against a child or young adult sets the agenda for their lives. Tolerant and wise parents do not throw possessions back at angry teenagers. Loving and well-ordered families temper frustration with a variety of de-escalation techniques, often by instinct and without training and jargon. Contented and tolerant parents were often happy children: they may have lied frequently to their parents but, when the chips were down, they could talk to them too, free from the risk of violence. Family tolerances are often stretched: any family with the experience of a member going through serious and irrational mental illness or distress will know how especially taut the family elastic may become in those circumstances. If, despite the important and necessary inhibitions of institutional settings, we can apply the best of instinctive and loving values to the institutional situation, then we shall be achieving something of value.

Changes in demography and improvements in health mean that much that we have learned in dealing with the young will have to be adapted and developed for the care of the growing elderly population. The effects of advanced dementia are often less of a challenge than the period of its development, when the rational and irrational are so interwoven that the degree of frustration can be very high, and with it anger and even violence can erupt.

Dr Rhidian Hughes and his team of contributors have brought together in this single volume a wealth of resource material and views across the range of age and conditions in which restraint has been and continues to be used. The premise of the book must be right: physical restraint has to be the last resort. Insufficient resources can never be a just excuse, and should never be a lawful reason for restricting the movement of a person for whom there is any realistic alternative. This is a recurring historical theme, a refrain produced by successive committees and reports over more than 200 years. Progress has been slow. Even the inclusion of the European Convention on Human Rights as an enforceable part of UK legal systems, following the Human Rights Act 1998, has not provided as powerful a catalyst as some of us expected in curtailing dramatically the use, misuse and even abuse of restraints. They have been taken for granted for too long.

The book includes a description of managed responses. These are responses tailored to the individual, person-centred and designed to ensure that the person concerned shares as far as is possible in his or her therapy and care. Even when there is significantly reduced mental capacity or insight, the role of experience is often underrated. Well-managed therapy and care, maximising the value of the client's experience, can often be used to make the use of restraint unnecessary. Strategy can maintain dignity, for carers and clients alike.

When all is read, one is left with the residual question as to how much legislative regulation is needed. The answer, probably, is some but not too much. The trouble with legislation, in the UK at least, is that it is tightly drawn and insufficiently purposive. However, any legislative gaps can be filled by clear and enforceable professional ethics, standards and review. Wherever the regulatory debate occurs in the wake of this volume, the balance between legislation and professional review will be a critical area for decision.

I commend this book as required reading, a most valuable contribution to a sensitive and important subject.

Alex Carlile
Gray's Inn
March 2009

Preface

For some time there has been concern about the use of restraint on people who use health and social care services. The term *restraint* is used to cover a wide range of activities by means of which an individual's freedom of movement is restricted. Challenging behaviours, organisational cultures and resource pressures all influence the use of restraint. The behaviours or situations that give rise to health and social care staff considering the use of restraint need to be understood, and there should be much greater awareness of therapeutic approaches, which are at the core of health and social care practice. The central premise underpinning this book is that any form of restraint should only be adopted in the most extreme cases and once all other options have been exhausted.

Internationally, much has been studied and written about the use of restraints. Themes from research and studies help to explain the use of restraint, as well as identifying propitious opportunities for therapeutic approaches. Professional bodies, the third sector, regulators and governments have also published guidance on the use of restraint. However, there is no consolidated resource to discuss the arising issues for practice and policy, especially within a UK context. This, the first edited book to examine restraint across health and social care settings, broadly identifies the key issues, describes trends and patterns and discusses tensions in practice and policy as well as seeking ways to address some of the critical and currently unresolved issues facing health and social care staff. The book blends a specific focus on individuals and groups alongside broader discussions of history, policy and practice. In an edited book such as this, there will inevitably be some overlap of the issues, some commonalities of views as well as contrasting perspectives. The purpose of editing this volume is not to standardise perspectives, but to provide a platform for discussion and debate. It is hoped these perspectives will bring opportunities for the development of positive practice as synergies are forged and there is some cross-fertilisation of ideas.

The idea for this book originated during my time at the regulator for social care in England, when I was charged to produce various reports, including one on restraints (Commission for Social Care Inspection, 2007). This particular report served its purpose – to raise discussion and debate about the use of restraints – and for me it also ignited an interest to understand more about the broader mosaic of restraints used across care services. This volume is a product of these interests. Putting together a volume of this kind requires the support of a group of experts who have all come together to offer their views and perspectives on restraint. Contributing to writing projects of this kind is rarely, if ever, part of substantive job roles, so I am very grateful to the authors for their time and effort spent in bringing the chapters to fruition.

Rhidian Hughes
Brighton
March 2009

Reference

Commission for Social Care Inspection (2007) *Rights, Risks and Restraints. An Exploration Into the Use of Restraint in the Care of Older People*. London, Commission for Social Care Inspection.

Contributors

Lord Carlile of Berriew Q.C.
Alex Carlile graduated LLB AKC at King's College London. He was called to the Bar by Gray's Inn in 1970. He is a Fellow of King's College London. He was appointed a Life Peer in 1999, and takes the Liberal Democrat Whip. He is involved in numerous charities. He is the President of the Howard League for Penal Reform. He has a particular interest in mental health issues, and was a co-founder of the Welsh charity Rekindle. He chaired the Select Committee of both Houses of Parliament on recent mental health legislation. He has written several reports. He was the author of *Too Serious a Thing*, a report published in 2002 on the safety of children in the NHS. His major report for the Howard League on the use of restraints on children in custody was published in February 2006.

Di Hart
Di Hart worked for many years as a social worker and manager before taking up a development post at the National Children's Bureau in 2002. She has a particular interest in children in secure settings. Recent projects include a review of physical restraint in secure children's homes, guidance on working with looked after children in custody and a toolkit aiming to improve outcomes for the children of drug-misusing parents.

Camilla Haw
Camilla Haw is currently a consultant psychiatrist at St Andrew's Hospital, Northampton, having previously worked in the NHS. She has published extensively on diverse aspects of psychiatric practice, including the rise and fall of the non-restraint movement in nineteenth century England and the current widespread use of psychiatric drugs for unlicensed indications (off-label prescribing). Another interest is the now common practice of antipsychotic polypharmacy for the treatment of schizophrenia, a strategy which remains largely unsupported by research findings.

Rhidian Hughes
Rhidian Hughes has degrees in social policy including a Doctorate from the University of York. He held a number of academic positions before working for

the social care regulator in England, the Commission for Social Care Inspection, during its existence between 2004 and 2009. At the Commission Rhidian was responsible for national investigations and reports which included the use of restraints. He holds honorary positions as Visiting Senior Lecturer at Guy's, King's and St Thomas' School of Medicine and Visiting Senior Researcher at the Institute of Gerontology, King's College London.

David Leadbetter

David Leadbetter is Director of CALM Training Services (Crisis Aggression, Limitation and Management). A former social work practitioner and trainer with a long-term research interest in violence management and challenging behaviour in human services, his professional background connects with his amateur involvement in martial arts teaching and practice. His organisation achieved the best results in the biggest restraint reduction project undertaken to date internationally. This federally funded restraint reduction project was initiated in response to the revelation of high levels of restraint injuries and fatalities in US human services, and was coordinated by the Child Welfare League of America. In addition to training, consultancy and policy development for organisations across the UK and abroad, he has been involved in a variety of research and national policy initiatives in the UK, Europe and the USA. He acts as an expert witness, has published extensively and is a regular contributor to international conferences.

Paul Linsley

Paul Linsley began his nursing career as a general nurse working within acute medicine. Following conversion to mental health nursing he gained valuable experience in a variety of clinical settings. Paul is registered as a Clinical Specialist in Acute Psychiatry and is trained in Cognitive Behavioural Therapy, as well as being a Lead Trainer in Conflict Resolution and Management. As a Senior Lecturer for the University of Lincoln he teaches on a number of courses: single and joint honours undergraduate programmes, research masters programmes and pre- and post-registration nurse training programmes.

Kevin McKenna

Kevin McKenna has more than 25 years' experience in various clinical settings in roles which have included practice, administration, education and research. In addition to professional training as a nurse he holds undergraduate degrees in Psychology and Health Administration and postgraduate degrees in Psychology and Education. He has led a number of national and international initiatives related to aggression and violence within healthcare, and is currently completing research on the clinical and organisational effectiveness of responses to the problem.

Gail Miller

Gail Miller is a registered mental health nurse with a degree in Cognitive Behavioural Therapy. She has over 20 years' experience working in services as a clinician, manager and tutor in the safe and therapeutic prevention and management of aggression and violence. Gail previously worked as mental health manager at NHS Security Management Service and was co-author, with Brodie Paterson, of the mandatory non-physical intervention training syllabus 'Promoting Safer and Therapeutic Services'. She is currently Associate Director for Risk Reduction at West London Mental Health Trust.

Brodie Paterson

Brodie Paterson is presently a Senior Lecturer at the Department of Nursing and Midwifery at the University of Stirling, where his interests include both research and teaching. His research and publication record is extensive and he has participated in a number of national and international projects involving policy development, research and training. He is a regular contributor to national and international conferences and has successfully completed a PhD.

Debbie Townsend

Debbie Townsend is the Physical Intervention Training Manager with the Ridgeway Partnership, providing training in the prevention and therapeutic management of challenging behaviour. Debbie has considerable experience as a community nurse for people who have a learning disability, challenging behaviour and mental health needs, and also with people who have neurological problems, head injuries, physical disabilities and autistic spectrum disorder.

John Turnbull

John Turnbull is the Performance, Information and Nursing Director with the Ridgeway Partnership and Visiting Professor in Learning Disability Nursing at the University of Northampton. He has over 25 years' experience as a manager, clinician and researcher in learning disability services, especially for people with challenging behaviour. He was the founding editor of *Learning Disability Practice* and spent two and a half years at the Department of Health as Nursing Officer for learning disability. He has been a specialist nurse adviser to the British Institute of Learning Disability.

Graeme Yorston

Graeme Yorston is a Consultant Forensic Psychiatrist at St Andrew's Hospital, Northampton, specialising in the assessment and treatment of older mentally disordered offenders and those with neuro-psychiatric problems. He has published on a range of topics, including psychopharmacology, psychiatric services for elderly offenders and the history of psychiatry, which he believes has much to offer in furthering our understanding of current controversies in mental health.

List of figures and tables

List of acronyms and abbreviations

BILD	British Institute of Learning Disabilities
C&R	Control & restraint
CAICA	Coalition Against Institutionalized Child Abuse
CALM	Crisis Aggression Limitation Management
CFSMS	Counter Fraud & Security Management Service
CoE	Council of Europe
CSCI	Commission for Social Care Inspection
CWLA	Child Welfare League of America
DCFS	Department for Children, Families and Skills
DH	Department of Health
HCHC	House of Commons Health Committee
HSE	Health and Safety Executive
NAO	National Audit Office
NASMHPD	National Association of State Mental Health Program Directors
NICE	National Institute for Clinical Excellence
NHS	National Health Service
NIMHE	National Institute for Mental Health in England
NPSA	National Patient Safety Agency
Ofsted	Office for Standards in Education, Children's Services and Skills
OPCS	Office of Population Censuses and Surveys
PCC	Physical control in care
PI	Physical intervention
PRN	*Pro re nata* ('when required')
RCN	Royal College of Nursing
RCP	Royal College of Psychiatrists
SAN	Secure accommodation network
SDE	Seated double embrace
SIRCC	Scottish Institute for Residential Child Care
STC	Secure training centre
TCI	Therapeutic crisis intervention
UK	United Kingdom
UN	United Nations

USA	United States of America
V&A	Violence & aggression
WAG	Welsh Assembly Government
WHO	World Health Organization
YJB	Youth Justice Board
YOI	Young offender institution

Reducing restraints in health and social care: an overview

Rhidian Hughes

Throughout this book the term *restraint* will refer to the restriction of some-one's freedom. To do so raises complex ethical and legal considerations for services, not least in the careful balance that needs to be struck between care and control and between risk and safety. The issues are rarely clear cut and it is difficult to suggest which responses are 'right' or 'wrong' without full appre-ciation of the wider context of 'real life' care. Instead, what is important here is an understanding of the issues that restraint raises and practice that places individuals' rights and wishes at the centre of all decision making.

This book has been produced so that the problems surrounding the use of restraints across a range of health and social care settings can be better under-stood. Ultimately it is hoped that the book will contribute, in some way, to levering improvements in how we understand restraint and practically in the care people receive. It is designed to appeal to a wide readership, including health and social care professionals, researchers, students and lecturers. Chap-ters assume no specialist knowledge.

Chapter 1, by Graeme Yorston and Camilla Haw, traces the use of restraints from the classic Greek-Roman period onwards. They are primarily concerned with mechanical restraints and note that, in the first hospitals, views on their use were divided. Interestingly, mechanical restraints received criticism from a government select committee as early as 1792 (and again in 1815). The non-restraint movement emerged at a time when more humane treatment of the 'insane' was encouraged, yet restraints continued to be employed neverthe-less. Pioneers of the movement emphasised keeping restraints to a minimum, which mirrored trends more widely in Europe. In contrast, restraints continued to be promoted in North America during the same period. Yorston and Haw demonstrate the move from mechanical restraints in the early nineteenth cen-tury to physical holding techniques that continue to be used today. They also comment on chemical and surgical restraints to manage mental illness. This chapter illustrates some of the linkages between past and current usages of

1

restraint and emphasises the value of looking at past debates to help inform our understanding of contemporary issues.

Following these historical perspectives, Chapter 2 (Hughes) provides a broad introduction to the current use of restraints across health and social care settings. It places restraint within a human rights framework, before going on to highlight briefly some definitions of restraint and the tensions in practice and policy. Some of the later chapters in this book will discuss restraint primarily with regard to physical restraints and interventions. However, from the outset it is important to recognise the wide range of ways in which an individual's freedom can be restricted. Chapter 2 therefore presents a working typology which captures both direct forms of restraint as well as methods that are more subtle and, perhaps, taken for granted – from physical restraint and interventions to electronic surveillance. The chapter goes on to locate restraints within a broader care context and emphasises the importance of understanding people's behaviour and involving them fully in decisions about their care. These principles are elaborated in later chapters.

The book moves to explore restraint from the perspectives of people who use health and social care services. Di Hart examines the use of physical restraint on children and young people in Chapter 3. She begins her analysis by raising concerns about the contradictory legal and policy frameworks, and comments on the absence of single criteria for restraint across children's services and care settings. She notes that any criteria will be interpreted during 'crisis points' and during these situations what constitutes the 'last resort' for one is not the same for another. Equally there is lack of consistency about methods in different service settings. Certain methods are prescribed in secure settings, for example, but there is limited guidance in other health and social care settings. Hart explores some of the ethical sensitivities of the different methods, with reference to studies that have explored children and young people's views and experiences. Issues for children and young people centre on the fair and appropriate use of restraints that are neither excessive nor punitive. Hart argues for restraint avoidance via improved behavioural management of children and young people coupled with positive organisational and care cultures. She concludes, 'the exercise of power must always be taken seriously and constantly questioned' and calls for a series of additional safeguards to be in place when restraints are used.

Physical restraint continues to be explored in Chapter 4 by John Turnbull and Debbie Townsend, who examine its use among adults with learning disabilities. They introduce their chapter by explaining about learning disabilities and the shift towards specialist community services in recent years. The chapter emphasises the importance of a managed response to challenging behaviour which involves keeping restraint to an absolute minimum. When restraint is applied it should be done with the highest regard to safety. Their positive practice model emphasises consistent, managed and proportionate responses.

In particular, involving people with learning disabilities in discussions about restraint is invaluable, not only because it helps to provide individualised care, but because it can also reduce fears that restraints are used punitively. Turnbull and Townsend elaborate how system-wide forces help to understand how notions of restraint are constructed. Here, studies show how improvements in care environments, together with a person-centred approach, can reduce restraint use. They go on to argue for a broader approach to therapy, which enables people with learning disabilities to regain control and be empowered to take positive steps to manage their own behaviour.

Paul Linsley addresses appropriate responses to violence from people with mental health needs in Chapter 5. He sketches out the mental health service context before going on to explore why people are restrained. The analysis recognises physical restraint as well as other procedures, including seclusion and sedation. For Linsley, nothing to do with restraint constitutes a good philosophy of care unless all other therapeutic approaches have failed. Furthermore, restraint can only be ethically defensible within a therapeutic environment; otherwise it risks being counter-productive and may preclude therapeutic benefits. Linsley draws our attention to the importance of sound policies and strategy coupled with senior management commitment as a means of reducing restraints in mental health services. Enabling people to make decisions for themselves is an important policy theme, not least because restraint can seriously compromise people's dignity when using services. These policy themes are picked up in the next chapter.

Chapter 6 (Hughes) looks at the restraint of older people, paying special attention to people with dementia. The chapter reviews the linkages between elder abuse and restraint before examining current policy priorities. A theme throughout this book, and emphasised here, is the promotion of people's independence and choice and the importance of understanding care needs from the perspective of the individual. Mental capacity legislation in the UK is especially relevant when considering restraint of people with dementia as it sets out clear guidance about when restraint is, and is not permissible. The chapter notes how little is known about the extent to which older people are subject to restraint, and discusses some of the issues to consider when older people's physical and cognitive abilities are impaired. The chapter explores how bedrails represent subtle restraint when used inappropriately. Better education and training for staff and improved management of resources are highlighted in conclusion.

Gail Miller, Brodie Paterson and Kevin McKenna begin Chapter 7 with an insightful case study which highlights how easily issues can escalate out of proportion and result in restraint. The contextual elements of care are well highlighted in the case study and borne out in the subsequent analyses. For example, they emphasise how violence is mediated by context, suggestive of an expression of disempowerment and injustice rather than a symptom of illness or impairment. The chapter examines the concept of 'zero tolerance', a product of recent health and safety campaigns and other initiatives, that aim to reduce violence against public sector staff. The chapter argues for the need to look beyond notions of zero tolerance to recognise the complex interplay between people's relationships and the organisational environment. Policy lessons and experience from the UK and Republic of Ireland are shared before the World Health Organization's framework is used to understand appropriate strategic responses: primary prevention, secondary resolution and de-escalation approaches and tertiary prevention to minimise and monitor restraint.

In the final chapter David Leadbetter and Brodie Paterson take a broader view and draw on international experience to illustrate key themes from policy and practice in the UK as well as from the USA. They acknowledge the limited research and evidence base on the frequency of restraint use, which may, in part, be due to the lack of regulation. This matter is coupled with considerable uncertainty around the application of restraint methods, especially methods deemed 'fragile'. They go on to discuss the factors important to reducing restraints: resources, leadership, recruitment and retention of well-trained staff and person-centred cultures of care together with the political and policy will for change. Leadbetter and Paterson conclude their chapter, and this book, with a fundamental question about restraint-free care, notably – do we want to? For to reduce restraints requires major improvements to be made to the quality of care that people receive as much as it does in taking direct practical steps to obviate restraints in all but the most extreme cases. And therein lie some of the critical issues for the further development of health and social care services.

CHAPTER I

Historical perspectives on restraint

Graeme Yorston and Camilla Haw

The use of restraint in health and social care settings remains a controversial topic. In 1838 Robert Gardiner Hill of the Lincoln Asylum declared 'in a properly constructed building, with a sufficient number of attendants, restraint is never necessary, never justifiable, and always injurious' (Belkin, 2002). Now, 170 years later, there is still little agreement on whether his views can be considered correct or not. One of the reasons for the lack of consensus is that there has been very little in the way of modern empirical research into current practice; another is the trend over the past half century to interpret the history of psychiatry in political terms. For many years, histories of psychiatry, written predominantly by retired clinicians, painted a comforting picture of the gradual emergence of a scientific discipline from the dark and barbaric practices of the eighteenth century, into the more enlightened and socially principled nineteenth century asylum era. From there, further steady progress, and the development of psychopharmacological treatments helped it attain its full maturity and equality with other medical specialties by the middle of the twentieth century. Then came Michel Foucault: highly influential and still much debated French philosopher, historian and critic of social institutions, including prisons and mental hospitals. His treatise *Folie et Déraison: Histoire de la Folie á l'Age Classique*, in its rather more snappily entitled English translation *Madness and Civilisation* was brought to the attention of Anglophone psychiatry in 1965 by no less a figure than R. D. Laing, Scottish psychiatrist and champion of the anti-psychiatry movement, noted for his views that the symptoms of psychotic patients could be interpreted as valid descriptions of lived experience rather than as signs of mental disorder. Foucault argued that rather than representing progress to a more humane way of dealing with the mentally ill, the creation of psychiatry was part of a systematic, state-sponsored policy to remove the economically inactive – the poor, the unemployed, prisoners and madmen – from society, in an act he referred to as a 'gigantic moral imprisonment'. Thought-provoking though Foucault's work was, the recent translation of the full version of his book, including its footnotes and sources, has revealed the scholarship on which it was based would not stand up to modern historical critical analysis (Scull, 2007). Contemporary research has now moved away from such grand philosophical concerns, returning to its roots, to examine primary sources for evidence of what actually went on in asylums. This research has shown that practice differed widely between mental institutions in the same country, and even more widely between different countries, resulting in a plurality of, sometimes conflicting, but all equally valid, histories of madness and its treatment. As an introduction to the discussions of the use of restraint in various clinical groups and care settings we will attempt to lay down a brief overview of the history of restraint.

The age of fetters

Classical Greek medicine, recorded in the *Corpus* of Hippocrates (*ca.* 460–370 BC), expounded the humoural theory that mental illness arose from an imbalance of the four humours, black bile, yellow bile, blood and phlegm. Melancholia was thought to be due to an excess of black bile, mania to an excess of blood. Imbalances were corrected by blood letting, purges and aperients. Hippocrates advocated humane treatments for the insane that included rest, bathing, exercise and dieting, but restraint of the mad who were considered dangerous to themselves or others, in their own homes, or by the use of chains and fetters, appears to have been common practice and there are a number of references to this in the classical literature (Vaughan, 1919).

The Roman physician Celsus (properly Aulus Cornelius Celsus *ca.* 25 BC–AD 50) further developed Greek medical thinking, noting that insanity could be brought on by fever and cured by whatever cured the fever. He advocated the use of restraints, to the extent of warning about their premature removal:

> ... those who conduct themselves more violently it is expedient to fetter, lest they should do harm either to themselves or to others. Anyone so fettered, although he talks rationally and pitifully when he wants his fetters removed, is not to be trusted, for that is a madman's trick (Celsus, tr. Spencer, 1938).

Furthermore, Celsus suggested that certain types of insanity were due to stubbornness and sufferers could be brought to their senses by pain-inducing treatments:

> If ... it is the mind that deceives the madman, he is best treated by certain tortures. When he says or does anything wrong, he is to be coerced

by starvation, fetters and flogging. He is to be forced both to fix his attention and to learn something and to memorize it; for thus it will be brought about that little by little he will be forced by fear to consider what he is doing (Celsus, tr. Spencer, 1938).

If this is one of the earliest recorded practice guidelines on the use of compulsion and restraint, in the writings of Soranus (AD 98–138), a Greek physician who practised in Alexandria and Rome, we find the earliest criticisms of restraint and an attempt at a more humanistic approach. Soranus dismissed the common treatments for madness at this time – confinement in a dark room, flogging, starvation, sedation with alcohol or opium – as futile. Instead, he recommended that patients should be kept in rooms with modest light and adequate warmth and always on the ground floor to prevent suicide attempts; that they should be put on a simple diet with regular exercise, and restrained only if necessary, and if so, with bonds made of wool or soft materials to prevent injury. He also recommended that to avoid unnecessary injury, the servants who restrained them should use their hands and not clubs or other instruments (Gerdtz, 1994).

As Northern Europe stumbled into the scientific shadows of the Dark Ages, classical learning was kept alive and further developed in the Islamic world. The first hospitals with separate wings for the mentally ill were built in the eighth and ninth centuries. Ibn Sina (980–1037, often known by his Latinised name of Avicenna), a Persian polymath and physician, was one of the first writers to consider internal psychological factors in mental illness. He did not view the insane as being possessed of demons or djinns and advocated the removal of patients' chains (Stone, 1997).

Hospitals for the physically ill began to appear in Europe from the thirteenth century onwards, but as there were few stone buildings available to anchor chains to at this time, furious and dangerous madmen were often confined in shackles in churches. For example, in 1286 a man who had killed a woman while deranged was confined in a church in Yarmouth (Walker, 1968). Europe's oldest psychiatric establishment, The Bethlem Hospital, was founded as the Priory of St Mary of Bethlehem in London in 1247. It is not clear exactly when it began to look after the insane, but by 1403 it had six lunatic patients (Andrews *et al.*, 1997). An inventory from 1398 lists four pairs of manacles, eleven chains of iron, six locks and keys and two pairs of stocks, suggesting that mechanical restraint was common (Scheerenberger, 1983), but as the institution also served as a bridewell or gaol, it is likely this hardware would also have been used on those detained other than for mental health reasons.

Felix Plater (1536–1614), a Swiss anatomist and taxonomist, was one of the earliest writers to attempt to classify mental illness according to symptoms. He also introduced the term *alienation* in his major work *Praxeos Medicae* in 1602, and for the next 300 years, psychiatrists were known as *alienists*. In an effort to better understand the conditions his patients had to endure, he lived in the cages and cells in which they were kept. Although he later decried the use of such harsh conditions, he did continue to recommend chains and the burning of the forehead to allow the release of demonic vapours for highly disturbed patients (Millon *et al.*, 2004).

Thomas Willis (1621–1725), English physician and inventor of the term *neurology*, declared that: 'Furious Madmen are sooner, and more certainly cured by punishments and hard usage, in a strait room, than by Physick or Medicines'. Moreover, he advocated that their 'diet be slender and not delicate, their cloathing coarse, their beds hard, and their handling severe and rigid' (Willis, 1684). The Archives of the Bethlem Hospital suggest that Willis's methods were very much in use at that time. A record of purchases for 1675, when there were 260 patients in the hospital, includes 60 leg locks and 12 handcuffs. However, Governors' Minutes from 1672 describe the case of Edward Purcell, who was confined by Royal Warrant and ordered to be 'kept in chaines & locked upp to prevent danger of fire & hurting the persons of the Officers there'. Despite several applications to discharge him, having been declared 'cured & recovered of his Lunacy', the Privy Council was slow in ordering his release. The Court eventually ordered that the chains be taken off and that he remain in the hospital with 'the Like Liberty as others there have'. That this case was highlighted by the governors suggests that his six months in irons was perhaps the exception rather than the rule, if only in the duration of his restraint (Andrews *et al.*, 1997). Nevertheless, concerns about the inhumane treatment of the insane in the largely private madhouses of eighteenth century England became increasingly vociferous. Patients and other concerned parties published pamphlets highlighting notorious cases. Ingram (1997) reproduces one such written by a Samuel Bruckshaw in 1774. In 'One More Proof of the Iniquitous Abuse of Private Madhouses', the former patient describes his treatment thus:

> They threw me upon my back on the bed, one of the men clapped his elbow upon my mouth and burst my lips against my teeth. They bled into my mouth and I was held down in such a manner that I was near being suffocated with blood ... They took out their bludgeons and came brandishing them over me. The next day they bound me hand and foot to the bed until the next morning ... without nourishment.

The scandals continued, and the Bethlem Hospital was heavily criticised in a Parliamentary Select Committee in 1792. Not all visitors saw cruelty and mismanagement, however; the German authoress Sophie van la Roche described her visit in 1786 thus:

> The forethought and humanity of Bethlem is exemplified in the manner of restraint: chains replaced by the strong jacket which obviates the

Figure 1.1 A man seated nude in chains, the prevailing character and physiognomy of a madman'. From Charles Bell (1824) *Essays on Expression*. (Reproduced with permission: Wellcome Library, London.)

tendency of chains and straps to rub sores if patients make frenzied gestures. It renders the insane harmless without having to suffer (Williams, 1933).

The Bethlem appointed a new apothecary, John Haslam, in 1795. However, he soon reverted to manacles and leg locks, considering the straight waistcoat 'too constricting and uncomfortably hot and provoking of perspiration' and that it prevented the patient from relieving irritation and inhibited his 'attention to cleanliness' (Andrews *et al.*, 1997).

The Age of Enlightenment and the emergence of the non-restraint movement

Throughout Europe and the Americas, the second half of the eighteenth century saw a revolution in philosophy, politics, education and religion. A belief in the power of reason and individual human rights and an increasing tendency to question the power of the Church and the aristocracy led to the obvious political changes in America and France, but also to smaller but no less significant changes in other countries. A better educated, better informed populace started to demand more of their governments. Against this background, Vincenzo Chiarugi (1759–1820), an Italian physician, published a three-volume treatise on madness entitled *Della Pazzia* in 1793–4. His humanitarian approach and disavowal of mechanical restraints predated the work of Pinel by several years. Nevertheless, he continued to recommend cloth and leather restraints, partly strengthened with iron, applied in a way that prevented sores or lacerations, and ties and handcuffs that permitted mobility rather than straitjackets. Although beatings were prohibited at his hospital, he advised that whipping around the waist could sometimes work for 'arrogant' manic patients (Gerard, 1998). At around the same time in France, Joseph Daquin (1733–1815) also proposed more humane treatment and the removal of patients' chains, but this went largely unnoticed (Fisher, 1994). Rather more well known is the story of Philippe Pinel (1745–1826), who, as the newly appointed physician at the Bicêtre Hospital in Paris in 1793, is said to have struck off the chains of the patients there, followed shortly after by those of the patients of the Salpêtrière, events immortalised in the famous 1876 painting by Tony Robert-Fleury.

The reality of these events is rather more complex, and it seems as if it was Jean-Baptiste Pussin, an ex-patient of the Bicêtre, later taken on as an assistant, who actually initiated the reforms in 1797, followed by Pinel three years later at the Salpêtrière (Weiner, 1992).

Attempts were also being made to establish more humane treatment of the insane in Britain at this time, most notably in the York Retreat founded

Figure 1.2 *Dr Pinel at the Salpêtrière*, by Tony Robert-Fleury (1876). (Reproduced with permission: Archives de l'Assistance Publique – Hôpitaux de Paris.)

Figure 1.3 *William Norris shackled on his bed at Bedlam,* by Ambroise Tardieu (1838). (Reproduced with permission: Wellcome Library, London.)

by William Tuke, a Quaker, in 1796. At the retreat, chains were removed and patients were housed in a pleasant environment, provided with decent food, and encouraged to busy themselves in a therapeutic programme of occupational tasks (Charland, 2007). Concerns that the proprietors of private madhouses were the main instigators of harsh and abusive treatment elsewhere had led to the Act for the Regulation of Private Madhouses in 1774, but continuing scandals led to the County Asylums Act of 1808, which was amended three times over the next ten years, and which enabled the setting up of public institutions for the insane. At the Bethlem Hospital, the case of James Norris, an American seaman who was held in a neck harness with chains no more than 12 inches long for 14 years, became publicised.

Another Parliamentary Select Committee was held in 1815 that savagely criticised the Hospital (Andrews *et al.*, 1997). By 1827, only nine counties had established asylums, so further Acts of Parliament followed in 1828. Finally in 1845 the Lunatics Act and the Lunatic Asylums and Pauper Lunatics Act were passed requiring each county to make provision for its insane, and establishing the Commissioners of Lunacy, an independent body to inspect all asylums to ensure proper and humane care and treatment (Jones, 1955).

Robert Gardiner Hill, House Surgeon, and Edward Charlesworth, Physician and Governor, at the Lincoln County Asylum, are generally regarded as being the pioneers of the non-restraint movement in the UK, having totally abolished the use of mechanical restraints at that institution by 1838 (Smith, 1999;

Lincolnshire Archives, 1838). John Connolly, who introduced non-restraint to the much larger Hanwell Asylum in the summer of 1839, and publicised the non-restraint movement, closely followed Lincoln (Hunter and Macalpine, 1963). However, Gardiner Hill himself suggested the credit for introducing non-restraint in its full extent should go to Thomas Prichard of the Northampton Asylum (Hill, 1857).

The Northampton Asylum (now St Andrew's Hospital) opened its doors to private and pauper lunatics on 1 August 1838. Founded by public subscription, it was originally built to take 82 patients, but like most asylums it was soon forced to expand, owing to pressure from the parishes to admit pauper lunatics. Thomas Prichard, the hospital's first Medical Superintendent, believed that insanity required prompt and early treatment in asylums to maximise patients' chances of recovery. He saw non-restraint as part of 'a system of kind and preventative treatment, in which all excitement is as much as possible avoided, and no care omitted' (Foss and Trick, 1989).

By October 1840, the Committee of the Northampton Asylum in their Second Annual Report reported that only a single patient had been 'subject (beyond temporary confinement in his room or the seclusion of a separate airing ground) to any species of mechanical restraint' and that this had occurred during Prichard's absence and was terminated by him on his return. Samuel Tuke of the York Retreat inspected the Northampton Asylum in October 1839 and wrote in the Visitors' Book 'I have visited this Establishment with much satisfaction. The entire absence of restraint, with the general prevalence of order and quiet, is very striking'. Prichard himself wrote in his Second Annual Report of 1840 that 'at the opening of this Establishment every patient was set at liberty immediately after admission'. However, later in the same report he contradicted himself when describing a male patient, who after admission, was placed in mechanical restraints for some months.

Using the original case records and hospital reports, Haw and Yorston (2004), found that Prichard kept the use of restraints to a minimum. Patients who were brought to the asylum in mechanical restraints were generally taken out of restraints on the night of admission, but in some cases temporary restraints were used subsequently to control violent behaviour. Instead, Prichard used solitary confinement, low rations and shower baths to control aggressive behaviour.

The case of Joseph Church supports Prichard's claims of non-restraint: he was a 31-year-old railroad labourer, admitted as a pauper lunatic from a workhouse on 1 August 1838 with his first attack of insanity, having been ill for two months. The case notes record how he had assaulted his wife and bitten her severely. 'After this he was restrained but escaped knocking down his keeper and scaling two high walls, he plunged into the canal and intentionally banged his head repeatedly with great violence against the bridge'. He had 'worn a strait-waistcoat for more than a week' prior to admission, but this was removed on arrival, and Prichard ordered that no restraints be used, but that he should be given a 'low diet', 'kept quiet and cool' and treated with digitalis, antimony tartrate and calomel (mercuryl chloride – used as a purgative). Two days after admission the patient asked to work in the garden and did so for more than an hour; within two weeks he was working 'daily in the garden from 9 in the morning until 6pm'. The patient was discharged 'recovered' two months after admission.

But the following case suggests that despite his best intentions, the staff still had to utilise restraints at times: Joseph Sturman, a 25-year-old labourer and pauper lunatic, was admitted on 24 August 1838 suffering from insanity caused by epilepsy. At the Bedford Asylum he was described as 'very violent and malicious, will fight, kick and bite. Not to be trusted with any safety to the attendants'. However, to Prichard he seemed 'perfectly sane in conversation and conduct'. He came in with 'iron leg locks and handcuffs'. An entry dated 10 September records: 'All restraint was removed on the night he was admitted ... Has been once or twice under restraint, a mild character when suffering not the effects of a rapid succession of fits but even then they were not on longer than a few hours'. Two subsequent entries state that no further use of restraint had been necessary and the patient was 'very industrious and useful'.

The available evidence therefore suggests that the abolition of mechanical restraints was a gradual process that occurred at the same time in a number of different institutions both in the UK and elsewhere in Europe, and that no single individual can be identified as the unequivocal initiator of this movement.

The situation in America was very different, where restraint continued to be used throughout the nineteenth century. Isaac Ray (1807–1881), Physician Superintendent of the Rhode Island Asylum and much praised for his humanity by his professional colleagues, was a staunch advocate of restraint. He said that Europeans tended to be obedient, whether insane or not, but, Americans with their greater love of liberty, were not so apt to be compliant, and therefore the 'attempt to abandon entirely the use of all means of personal restraint is not sanctioned by the true interests of the insane' (Tomes, 1988).

Safe patient restraint

Even though the manacles, leg locks and handcuffs and straitjackets began to disappear from European psychiatry at the beginning of the nineteenth century, the lack of understanding of the causes of mental illness led to a burgeoning of mechanical 'treatments', including suspension, rotation, immersion in water, abrasion and countless others, which even if not initiated with the primary goal of restraining the agitated patient must surely have had this as a second-ary benefit. To say that the disappearance of the ironmongery of mechani-cal restraint over the course of the nineteenth century meant that patients no longer had physical limitations placed on their liberty would be wrong. What gradually took the place of mechanical restraint was the physical holding down of patients, and this has continued up to the present day in British psychia-try (Stubbs *et al.*, 2009). Because of concerns that safe patient restraint can be traumatising, both in the sense of causing bodily injury to the restrainer as well as the restrained (including death as in the case of 'Rocky' Bennett; Norfolk, Suffolk and Cambridgeshire Strategic Health Authority, 2004) and in the sense of re-traumatising individuals who may have been subjected to sexual abuse, there has been increasing criticism of the lack of standardisation of training and the poor evidence base for physical interventions in general. There is also a trend for mechanical restraining belts and other devices to be making a comeback in British secure hospitals.

Chemical restraint

Chemical restraint is not a new phenomenon: nineteenth century psychiatrists had access to morphine, bromide, chloral hydrate, paraldehyde, sulphanal and hyoscine as well as alcohol and opium. Before that, digitalis was used to calm manic patients (Williams, 1866). As early as 1895 Henry Maudsley said of mechanical restraint, that '... it may be doubted whether its coarse bonds did as much harm as has been done by the finer means of chemical restraint which have been used to paralyse the brain and render the patient quiet' (Braslow, 1999). More recently, Sidney Gelman (2000) has argued that the entire psy-chopharmaceutical industry is based on fundamentally flawed research, which values sedation above symptomatic relief. Although Gelman overstates his case, suspicions that the industry may not be as patient-focused as it would wish people to believe are widespread amongst mental health professionals.

Chlorpromazine (known as thorazine in the USA) was first used in psychi-atry in 1952 and was in widespread use by 1955. It was found to act on many different receptors in the brain (leading to some unfortunate side-effects) and so was given the proprietary name Largactil. The introduction of chlorpro-mazine heralded a new era in the treatment of the mentally ill, and for the first time many chronically ill patients with schizophrenia, long forgotten on the back wards of mental hospitals around the world, showed signs of improvement (Turner, 2007). Enthusiasm for the 'chemical cosh', as it was soon nicknamed, was based not only on its antipsychotic properties but also its ability to sedate excited and aroused (and troublesome) patients. Several other compounds followed rapidly, all of which did roughly the same thing, all useful, though sometimes producing distressing side-effects. All fell short of the Holy Grail of curing every patient. Even clozapine, an antipsychotic licensed specifically for treatment-resistant schizophrenia, failed to relieve some patients of their distressing symptoms and also carried with it the risk of potentially fatal suppression of white blood cells. Therapeutic optimism turned to frustration and then to desperation. In an effort to treat those patients who were not responding, and who could not be discharged from the ever-shrinking mental hospitals, psychiatrists prescribed higher and higher doses of antipsychotics, five or more times the licensing authorities' maximum recommended doses. When this was shown to be both of limited benefit and potentially toxic, with a number of unexpected deaths being attributed to it, psychiatrists switched to polypharmacy – prescribing two or three different antipsychotic agents at the same time – a practice that shares with high-dose prescribing a tenuous evidence base and serious potential for harm (the only exception being the use of clozapine combined with another antipsychotic, a strategy that can be helpful but is not without risk) (Stahl, 2004; Royal College of Psychiatrists, 2006).

The use of antipsychotics has been extended to other conditions beyond their marketing authorisations and often way beyond the research base, for example for the control of agitation in older people with dementia and people with learning disabilities, and children and adolescents with conduct disorders (Haw and Stubbs, 2007). Concerns about antipsychotic drug toxicity have led in recent years to much stricter safety guidelines, yet even the tight strictures of rapid tranquillisation are stretched through its use in patients with personality disorder (Hyde *et al.*, 1998), who by definition do not have a psychotic illness.

Surgical restraint

Though perhaps not often considered alongside other forms of restraint, the widespread use of pre-frontal lobotomy in the 1940s to render aggressive patients more compliant and docile could be regarded as restraint in the same way as medication. Though now largely discredited, the scale of the lobotomy industry at its peak was staggering. It is estimated that over 18,000 lobotomies were carried out in the USA (Valenstein, 1986), and it is somewhat ironic that the father of the procedure, Egaz Moniz (1874–1955), is still the only person to win the Nobel Prize for his work in psychiatry. Walter Freeman (1895–1972) introduced the procedure to the USA and developed a rapid transorbital method of carrying it out, nicknamed the 'ice-pick lobotomy', which took seven minutes to carry out. He personally carried out 3,500 procedures, achieving almost cult celebrity status through stunts such as performing the operation on both eye sockets at the same time, holding one *orbitoclast* in each hand. After the introduction of chlorpromazine the procedure became less popular, but Freeman spent the rest of his career travelling around the US in his *lobotomobile* visiting former patients (El-Hai, 2005).

An even more dramatic example of the abuse of mentally ill patients through surgery occurred as a result of the hypothesis that small pockets of infection (septic foci) could cause mental illness, and their removal could cure it. This was taken to extremes in the early years of the twentieth century by Henry Cotton (1876–1933), Medical Director of the New Jersey State Hospital. At first, patients had their teeth removed. If this failed to bring about improvement, a tonsillectomy and washout of the sinuses was recommended. If a cure was still not achieved, other organs were targeted in an ever more desperate attempt to rid the individual of their sepsis: the gall bladder, stomach, spleen, cervix, testicles, ovaries and the colon. A number of hospitals in North America wholeheartedly adopted Cotton's practices, along with several in the UK. Lauded in his time, partly because of his outrageously unrealistic claims of cure rates, Cotton eventually admitted there was a significant mortality from post-operative complications associated with surgery (contemporary analysis of his figures suggested that as many as 45% died following colectomy), and the practice was abandoned (Scull, 2006).

Conclusion

We can look back at the long history of restraint in the treatment of the mentally ill and shake our heads at the barbarity of some of the practices. Yet there remain wide variations in what currently goes on in hospitals even across the developed world. New cases of patients being found in cages continue to emerge (Sparks, 2004), mechanical restraint devices continue to be widely used in the USA, and restraining belts are starting to gain currency again in the UK. In care homes for older people, though the infamous Buxton chair may have now have all but disappeared, cot sides, tray attachments to chairs, and low or tilted seating all continue to be widely used. In modern psychiatry, although the use of mechanical restraints has largely been superseded by the more covert (and at first sight more acceptable) use of chemical restraint, we must not become complacent and think that the restraint debate is a topic of historical enquiry only. It is a debate that is very much part of twenty-first century health and social care.

References

Andrews, J., Briggs, A., Porter, R., Tucker, P. and Waddington, K. (1997) *The History of Bethlem*. Routledge, London.

Belkin, G. S. (2002) Self-restraint, self-examination: a historical perspective on restraints and ethics in psychiatry. *Psychiatric Services*, **53**(6), 663–4.

Braslow, J. T. (1999) History and evidence-based medicine: lessons from the history of somatic treatments from the 1900s to the 1950s. *Mental Health Services Research*, **1**(4), 231–40.

Celsus translated by Spencer, W. G. (1938) *On Medicine – Book III*. Loeb Classical Library, Heinemann, London.

Charland, L. C. (2007) Benevolent theory: moral treatment at the York Retreat. *History of Psychiatry*, **18**(1), 61–80.

El-Hai, J. (2005) *The Lobotomist: a Maverick Medical Genius and His Tragic Quest to Rid the World of Mental Illness*. Wiley, London.

Fisher, W. A. (1994) Restraint and seclusion: a review of the literature. *American Journal of Psychiatry*, **151**(11), 1584–91.

Foss, A. and Trick, K. (1989) *St. Andrew's Hospital, Northampton. The First 150 Years (1838–1988)*. Granta Editions, Cambridge.

Foucault, M. (1961) *Folie et Déraison: Histoire de la Folie á l'Age Classique*. Paris, Plon. Translated and abridged as *Madness and Civilisation: A History of Insanity in the Age of Reason* by R. Howard (London: Tavistock, 1965). Unabridged translation: *History of Madness* (ed. Jean Khalfa, transl. Jonathan Murphy and Jean Khalfa) (2006) Routledge, London.

Gelman, S. (2000) *Medicating Schizophrenia: a History*. Rutgers University Press, New Brunswick.

Gerard, D. L. (1998) Chiarugi and Pinel considered: Soul's brain/person's mind. *Journal of the History of the Behavioral Sciences*, **33**(4), 381–403.

Gerdtz, J. (1994) Mental illness and the Roman physician: the legacy of Soranus of Ephesus. *Hospital and Community Psychiatry*, **45**(5), 485–7.

Haw, C. and Stubbs, J. (2007) Off-label use of antipsychotics: are we mad? *Expert Opinion in Drug Safety*, **6**(5), 533–45.

Haw, C. and Yorston, G. (2004) Thomas Prichard and the non-restraint movement at the Northampton Asylum. *Psychiatric Bulletin*, **28**(4), 140–2.

Hill, R. G. (1857) *A Concise History of the Entire Abolition of Mechanical Restraint in the Treatment of the Insane*. Longman, London.

Hunter, R. and Macalpine, I. (1963) *Three Hundred Years of Psychiatry*. Oxford University Press, London.

Hyde, C. A., Harrower-Wilson, C. and Morris, J. (1998) Violence, dissatisfaction and rapid tranquilisation in psychiatric intensive care. *Psychiatric Bulletin*, **22**(8), 477–80.

Ingram, A. (1997) *Voices of Madness*. Sutton, Thrupp, Gloucestershire.

Jones, K. (1955) *Lunacy, Law and Conscience 1744–1845*. Routledge and Kegan Paul, London.

Lincolnshire Archives (1841) Hospl/St.John's/4/1/2. Lincoln Lunatic Asylum 17th Report.

Millon, T., Grossman, S. and Meagher, S. E. (2004) *Masters of the Mind: Exploring the Story of Mental Illness from Ancient Times to the New Millennium.* Wiley, London.

Norfolk, Suffolk and Cambridgeshire Strategic Health Authority (2004) *Independent Inquiry into the Death of David Bennett.* http://www.nscha.nhs.uk/4856/11516/David%20Bennett%20Inquiry.pdf (accessed 1 March 2009).

Northampton Record Office (1840). *Second Annual Report of the Northampton General Lunatic Asylum.* Westbrook, Wellingborough.

Robinson, G. (1859) *The Prevention and Treatment of Mental Disorders.* Longman, Brown, Green, Longmans and Roberts, London.

Royal College of Psychiatrists (2006) *Consensus Statement on High-dose Antipsychotic Medication.* Council Report CR138. http://www.rcpsych.ac.uk/files/pdfversion/CR138.pdf (accessed 1 March 2009).

St. Andrew's Hospital Archives. CL1.

Scheerenberger, R. C. (1983) *A History of Mental Retardation.* Brookes, Baltimore.

Scull, A. (2006) *Madhouse: a Tragic Tale of Megalomania and Modern Medicine.* Yale University Press, New Haven, Connecticut.

Scull, A. (2007) The fictions of Foucault's scholarship. *Times Literary Supplement On Line.* http://www.tlstimeonline.co.uk/article/0,,25347-2626687,00 (accessed 1 March 2009).

Smith, L. (1999) *Cure, Comfort and Safe Custody.* Leicester University Press, London.

Sparks, J. (2004) Ordeal of the caged Czech children http://www.timesonline.co.uk/tol/news/uk/health/article445266.ece?token'null&offset'0&page'1 (accessed 1 March 2009).

Stahl, S. M. (2004) Focus on antipsychotic polypharmacy: evidence-based prescribing or prescribing-based evidence? *International Journal of Neuropsychopharmacology,* **7**(2), 113–16.

Stone, M. H. (1997) *Healing the Mind: a History of Psychiatry from Antiquity to the Present.* Pimlico, London.

Stubbs, B., Leadbetter, D., Paterson, B., Yorston, G., Knight, C. and Davis, S. (2009) Physical intervention: a review of the literature on its use, staff and patient views and the impact of training. *Journal of Psychiatric and Mental Health Nursing,* **16**(1), 99–105.

Tomes, N. (1988) The great restraint controversy: a comparative perspective on Anglo-American psychiatry in the nineteenth century. In: *The Anatomy of Madness Volume III: The Asylum and its Psychiatry* (eds. W. F. Bynum, R. Porter and M. Shepherd). Routledge, London

Turner, T. (2007) Chlorpromazine: unlocking psychosis. *British Medical Journal,* **334**(Suppl.1), s7.

Valenstein, E. S. (1986) *Great and Desperate Cures.* Basic Books, New York.

Vaughan, A. C. (1919) *Madness in Greek Custom and Thought.* JH Furst and Co., Baltimore.

Walker, N. (1968) *Crime and Insanity in England I: The Historical Perspective.* Edinburgh University Press, Edinburgh.

Weiner, D. B. (1992) Philippe Pinel's 'Memoir on Madness' of December 11, 1774: a fundamental text of modern psychiatry. *American Journal of Psychiatry,* **149**(6), 725–32.

Williams, C. (1933) (editor and translator) *Sophie in London, 1786, Being the Diary of Sophie van la Roche*. Jonathan Cape, London.

Williams, S. W. D. (1866) Cases illustrating the use of digitalis in the treatment of mania, recent and chronic. *Journal of Mental Science*, **11**(56), 556–71.

Willis, T. (1684) *The Practice of Physick: Two Discourses Concerning the Soul of Brutes*. Dring, Harper, and Leigh, London. Quoted in Scull, A. (1989) *Social Order/Mental Disorder: Anglo-American Psychiatry in Historical Perspective*. University of California Press, Berkeley.

CHAPTER 2

Putting restraint in context

Rhidian Hughes

The only bond worth anything between human beings is their human-ness

Jesse Owens

Rights and restraint

The principles set out in the Universal Declaration of Human Rights, the European Convention on Human Rights and similar instruments encourage fairness, respect, equality, dignity and autonomy for all. In the UK the Human Rights Act 1998 makes these rights legally binding. The principles underpinning these rights reflect basic needs that enable us all to live full lives with maximum dignity and respect. These core societal values are at the heart of high-quality health and social care. Individuals should be put at the centre of all decisions about their care. In doing so, people's experiences of care, the quality of their lives, and their health and well-being can be improved.

The Human Rights Act places a legal obligation on services to respect human rights. All health and social care services need to be attuned to human rights and should ensure that its principles are meaningfully integrated into the routines of practice. There are some human rights that are particularly relevant to the health and social care context, including the right to life; freedom from torture, inhuman and degrading treatment and punishment; the right to liberty; the right to no punishment without law; and the right to respect for private and family life. Additional conventions – such as the United Nations (UN) Convention on the Rights of the Child and the UN Convention on the Rights of Persons with Disabilities – are not legally enforceable, but the UK has committed to their implementation.

Clearly, restraint has the potential to infringe both people's human rights and international conventions. The covert use of medication represents potential violation of the right not to be treated in an inhuman or degrading way. Similarly, the right to private and family life may be infringed if someone is subject to electronic tagging or tracking without informed consent. There may also be some forms of restraint that may not breach adults' rights, but may well breach those of children and young people (Hart and Howell, 2004). The UN Convention on the Rights of the Child, for example, emphasises that care should take account of children's best interests, age and development, and some forms of restraint, such as painful 'distraction' techniques used with young people reflect a probable breach in these respects (Carlile, 2006). The UK Children's Commissioners (2008) have expressed concern that continuing to allow physical restraint for the purposes of 'good order' in secure settings for children might encourage wider use of restraint. Commissioners also raised concerns about continued use of segregation for children in custody.

Some people who use health and social care services, especially those who are viewed by society as 'vulnerable', 'challenging' or whose voices are seldom heard or listened to can be seen as problems to be managed. When people use services there is a risk they may be treated differently and have their human and civil rights infringed. These different practices may be justified because of individuals' conditions and behaviour. People with dementia, for example, are one such group. There is a tendency for those in the advanced stages of dementia to be regarded by society as 'non-persons' without the rights and attributes that full citizenship implies. Thus, when someone with dementia moves into a care home, for example, it can accentuate views that those with dementia are not full citizens and certain freedoms are not as important for them as they are to the rest of society. The human rights 'lens' shows how these kinds of views are unfair and discriminatory. When adults use health and social care services, they have the right to total freedom, to do what they want and to go where they want, unless their liberties are restricted by law, for example being detained under the Mental Health Act 1983 (as amended).

Human rights practice seeks to reduce, and ultimately remove, unfair treatment, discrimination of individuals and structural inequalities in communities. Human rights therefore are not just legal issues but are a tool for more broader social and cultural change (British Institute of Human Rights, 2008). A human rights perspective can help to challenge social and cultural understandings about practice and policies and the discourses that shape the care and treatment people receive. A concern raised in the literature about the use of restraint is that people are not being fully involved in decisions about their care, including when restraints are applied. A consultation on the use of restraints with children and young people for example, emphasised that they did not know they would be restrained until it actually happened (Morgan, 2004). A human rights approach supports the deep and meaningful involvement of individuals in decisions about their own care as well as people taking steps to influence policies and practices more widely (Department of Health (DH), 2007).

Commentators have argued that there is not yet a culture of respect for human rights in the UK (Economic and Social Research Council, 2007). They call for human rights to be mainstreamed within services and for the public to be more aware of these rights. Commentators have also criticised the UK's narrow approach to human rights as serving only to protect civil and political rights. Broader social, cultural and economic rights – as set out by the UN International Covenant on Economic, Social and Cultural Rights – also need to be considered. These broader rights emphasise that people should have the opportunity to receive the highest standards of health and well-being and this requires excellent health and social care services. The quality of a service is likely to play an important determining role in how difficult situations that might give rise to the use of restraint are handled and – crucially – whether therapeutic approaches take precedent and become the norm over restraining ones.

Defining restraint

In its broadest sense, restraint is about preventing individuals from doing something they wish to do, including placing limits on people's will or ability. Some actions are clearly regarded as restraint, such as locking someone within a room to prevent them from leaving. Whereas other activities are subtler and less easy to define, such as the use of an electronic surveillance device to monitor someone's whereabouts.

There are a host of definitions of restraint stemming from professional guidance, research and Governments, all with reference to a wide range of care settings. Definitions need to encompass both legal definitions of restraint as well as including practices that place restrictions on people's lives in health and social care settings. A broad definition can help to recognise the ways in which restrictions are placed on people's freedom to live as they want but may be too general to recognise more subtle forms of restraint. Conversely, narrow definitions risk encouraging precision in practice.

> Any device, material or equipment attached to or near a person's body and which cannot be controlled or easily removed by the person and which deliberately prevents or is deliberately intended to prevent a person's free body movement to a position of choice and/or a person's normal access to their body (Retsas, 1998).

More specific definitions define particular forms of restraint, such as the covert administration of drugs and medication:

Chemical restraint describes both deliberate and incidental use of pharmaceutical products to control behaviour and/or restrict freedom of movement, but which is not required to treat a medically identified condition. These drugs may be purposively administered to sedate a patient as a means of convenience. Convenience is any action not in the patient's best interests to control or manage behaviour (Mott *et al.*, 2005).

In schools, the use of force to control and restrain pupils is less clearly defined and here the focus on proportionate approaches that balance reasonable force and outcomes:

There is no legal definition of when it is reasonable to use force. That will always depend on the precise circumstances of individual cases. To be judged lawful, the force used would need to be in proportion to the consequences it is intended to prevent. The degree of force used should be the minimum needed to achieve the desired result (Department for Children, Schools and Families, 2007).

For children and young people there are no clear criteria for when restraint should be used (see Chapter 3).

Different forms of restraint

How restraint is defined will influence how forms and categories of restraint are understood. The British Institute of Learning Disabilities (BILD) policy framework on physical interventions focuses on the use of direct physical force to some degree that restricts people's mobility. BILD categorises physical interventions into direct physical contact (i.e. an individual is physically controlled by another person, such as holding), the use of barriers (e.g. locked doors) and the use of materials or equipment (e.g. splints on people's arms to prevent movement) (Harris *et al.*, 2008). In the literature, restraint commonly refers to physical restrictions. However, when considering the use of restraint across a wide range of health and social care contexts, it is important to take a broad view on the ways freedom may be curtailed. A broad view covers clinical, environmental, organisational and cultural influences and encapsulates both overt forms of restraint as well as subtler forms. Different forms of restraint are not mutually exclusive and the preliminary typology presented here covers:

- physical restraints
- physical interventions
- covert medication and chemical restraint
- medical restraints
- environmental restraints
- seclusion
- aversive care practices
- surveillance: tagging and tracking

Physical restraints

Physical restraints prevent someone from moving as they wish. It might include tying or securing someone so they cannot move freely. An investigation into services for people with learning disabilities found high levels of use of physical restraints. For example, people were strapped to wheelchairs (to prevent them picking things up from the floor) and restrained in tilting chairs that were difficult to get out of.

> An advocate said they saw the individual being restrained in the chair while staff put Christmas decorations up. A review of records indicated that the man had been restrained in this chair on 33 occasions during a ten month period usually for 10 to 15 minutes and sometimes for up to 30 minutes (Healthcare Commission, 2007a).

Physical intervention

Moving someone against their will, pushing or the use of holding techniques (e.g. prone, surpine and basket holds) are examples of direct physical intervention. These forms of restraint may also involve some form of pain to encourage people to comply with the intervention. Physical intervention may also use 'distraction' techniques, which involve the infliction of pain on various parts of the body. Physical interventions that involve or rely on the use of pain as a means of control is a form of corporal punishment and arguably a breach of individuals' human rights. The UN (2002) has criticised the UK for its use of these kinds of techniques with children and young people. An inquiry into the use of restraints on children and young people in secure settings indicated that the deliberate infliction of pain could constitute a criminal offence (Carlile, 2006). The use of physical interventions, including prone restraints, has also been implicated in a number of restraint-related deaths (Paterson *et al.*, 2003; Ball, 2005).

Covert medication and chemical restraint

The use of major or minor tranquillisers (neuroleptics or antipsychotics, anxiolytics or benzodiazepines) plays a role in the clinical management of a range of psychiatric conditions, such as depression, hallucinations and delusion. The side-effects of these drugs, generally referred to as neuroleptic medication, can sedate and make people drowsy, docile and compliant, sometimes with reduced mobility. Covert medication and chemical restraint involves the use of drugs to change someone's behaviour. Neuroleptic medication may be prescribed 'when required' (also known by the Latin term *pro re nata* or PRN). PRN medication should only be prescribed for use in clearly defined clinical situations, yet vague PRN instructions by prescribers leave the administration of these drugs open to abuse in some settings. Concerns have been raised about the over-reliance on the use of drugs and the use of anticipatory prescribing to prevent issues from arising rather than dealing with issues as and when they arise (House of Commons Health Committee, 2004). A parliamentary committee heard that up to 70 per cent of prescribing was not appropriate for people with dementia (All Party Parliamentary Group on Dementia, 2008). Similarly, an investigation into services for people with learning disabilities illustrates how inappropriate use of drugs can help staff to manage their practice:

> ... a person was given PRN medication because he was impatient for his dinner and became distressed. The medication caused the person to become too sleepy to eat his dinner at what staff considered to be 'the right time' (Healthcare Commission and Commission for Social Care Inspection, 2006).

Covert medication can be lawful when people are detained under mental health legislation.

Medical restraints

Staff may take steps to prevent individuals from interfering with clinical or medical interventions that are designed to assist them and may compromise their clinical care and outcomes. For example, hand mittens are used to prevent people who are recovering from stroke from tugging or snagging their feeding tubes. These are undoubtedly controversial techniques that restrict people's freedom of movement. As Horsburgh *et al.* (2008) note, it is important for feeding tubes not to be dislodged to prevent feed fluid entering the lungs, to keep people well nourished and to prevent discomfort from continual reinsertion of the tubes. Horsburgh *et al.* (2008) argue that the use of mittens in these cases is 'a necessary evil'.

The use of restraints is especially problematic when they are used for extended periods and become routine rather than exceptional practice. The Healthcare Commission (2007a), for example, found that splints were used to prevent people routinely putting their hands or items in their mouths and these splints were only released for 30 minutes per day. Medical interventions may also involve some form of forced care. Interventions beyond strong persuasion and the force feeding of people with anorexia provide one example of forced care (Carney *et al.*, 2008). A second example is the use of rapid tranquillisation on psychiatric wards, as May (2005) recounts:

> Most first admissions to psychiatric hospital are characterised by a 'try this medication or if you don't we'll have to force you to take it' approach. ... Forced Acuphase [antipsychotic drug the side effect is sedation] is where a person is pinned down and undressed so that his or her buttocks are revealed. The person is then given a psychiatric cocktail ... which is administered by hypodermic syringe into the person's buttock.

Environmental restraints

The design and make-up of environments can limit people's abilities to move freely, such as locked doors, 'baffle' locks, complicated door handles, stair gates or disguised entrances and exits (e.g. using mirrors). A care home inspection report illustrates these kinds of environmental restraints at work:

> In order to 'contain' residents within the premises there is an unusually high number of locks and physical bars to free movement. There are four stair gates, six keypad locks and four baffle locks; staff routinely lock nine bedroom doors when the resident is not in the room. The cumulative effect is that many residents are somewhat corralled into the communal areas on the ground floor whilst others are room-bound and relatively isolated. The door to the conservatory has no door furni-

ture so most residents are unable to travel through easily; several were seen fumbling and then giving up. Such high levels of restraint do not suggest an effective framework for residents retaining adequate control over their lives and daily routines and has overtones of a secure facility (inspection report cited in CSCI, 2007).

Seclusion

Seclusion is 'the restriction of a person's freedom of association, without his or her consent, by locking him or her in a room' (Mental Welfare Commission for Scotland, 2007). The use of seclusion, effectively a form of solitary confinement, is used across health and social care services for people with learning disabilities (Healthcare Commission, 2007b) and for children and young people in secure settings (Carlile, 2006) and in care homes (CSCI, 2007). Seclusion tends to be used for punitive reasons, as a national audit of healthcare services for people with learning difficulties found:

> Interviews with patients and staff demonstrated that the seclusion/de-escalation room was used for any episode of 'bad behaviour' and could last anything up to one hour ten minutes. The records entered in an individual's case notes showed that patients were sent to the seclusion/de-escalation rooms as a result of 'bad behaviour'. There was no evidence that any of the patients sent to seclusion were cautioned under the requirements of mental health legislation for deprivation of liberty (Healthcare Commission, 2007b).

Aversive care practices

Aversive care practices change people's behaviour and may include, for example, unpleasant sensory or verbal stimuli to manage people's behaviour. Behaviour may be controlled by lights being turned off to discourage certain forms of activities. Threatening or dominant tones of voice to manage behaviour in some way may also be used. A study of people with dementia living in care homes illustrated how behaviour could be managed in this subtle way:

One staff member prevented some people moving around by placing their hands on their Zimmer [walking] frames and asking several times where people were going, which resulted in some people looking anxious and submissively sitting back down again (inspection report cited in CSCI, 2008).

Surveillance: tagging and tracking

Surveillance via electronic tagging and tracking or other devices has been proposed as part of a wider debate about the 'monitoring' of people. The use of this technology originates in secure settings, but discussion and debate have increasingly focused on people with dementia who may persistently walk (or 'wander') and people with learning disabilities (Welsh *et al.*, 2003). There are two main forms of surveillance: boundary alarms can be used to signal when people breach care home or hospital areas and tracking can be used with global positioning systems and mobile phone technology to track and monitor people's exact locations. The use of surveillance and tracking technology in health and social care in the UK is in its relative infancy, especially when compared with international developments. However, it is an area in which testing and acceptance studies are being conducted and therefore remains an important part of any discussion about the different forms that restraint can take. Similar issues are raised by the use of technology in 'smart' homes when people's movements are monitored and via the use of closed circuit television (CCTV) to provide timely care interventions.

The Alzheimer's Society (2007) have discussed the ethical and practical issues that must be explored when considering the use of this technology in care settings for people with dementia. They highlight the complexities of gaining consent for people with dementia and highlight some of the difficult questions that need to be addressed. For example, can consent only be obtained before the illness progresses to the 'later stages'? The Alzheimer's Society highlights the importance of advance directives in dementia care to ensure people's views are known well in advance. Other commentators have compared the use of technology and surveillance with more direct forms of restraint, noting that electronic technologies may offer the least restrictive option.

Privacy is clearly breached in any surveillance process, but if applied with the intention of maintaining a person at home, or free from a locked door in residential settings, where is the greater breach of rights? (Welsh *et al.*, 2003)

Looking beyond restraint

There are, therefore, a wide range of ways in which people's freedoms can be restricted by those responsible for their care. In adopting a broad view of restraint, as presented here, the boundaries around the term *restraint* also need to be made clear. First, we all have constraints on our lives, and people using services may well face some imposition of routine on their lifestyles. Set periods for certain activities (e.g. mealtimes), the banning of certain behaviours (e.g. smoking) and some areas in care settings that are out of bounds (e.g. staff rooms) are conditions of residence in some care homes, for example. These constraints fall outside the scope of most definitions of restraint, even though they may in some way limit people's freedoms.

Second, it is also important to recognise that the use of restraint can be a reflection of poor-quality care. Restraint may become embroiled in discussions about poor-quality care when inappropriate restraint practices become routinised into care, especially when there are insufficient reviews, policies and protocols in place.

Third, there will be situations when restraining actions go beyond poor-quality care and are simply abusive. At all levels child and adult abuse is an affront to human dignity and people's rights. It is not uncommon for debate about the use of restraint in the media to centre on the abuse of an individual or group 'at the hands of' staff 'behind closed doors'. Restraint is undoubtedly one of society's 'sensitive' topics, and one that also raises people's emotions as it relates closely to safeguarding and system failures. Discussions of human rights are, rightly, evoked when we learn about deaths associated with the use of particular forms of restraint, people being locked up and contained within residential care settings or simply being denied some freedom of movement without justifiable reason. Any unjustified forms of restraint should be investigated and given the full attention of the relevant regulatory and legal agencies. The use of restraint tends to grab the media spotlight. *Prima facie* it can be difficult to understand why restraints are used and emotive and sensational 'shock horror' vocabulary is commonly used to explain the various actions taken by staff. But these reactions are not always helpful if we are to develop a meaningful understanding about the ways in which people's freedoms are restricted and the effect this has on people and, crucially, where the balances need to be struck between care, freedom, safety and risks.

The debate about restraint-free care

Some commentators view any form of restraint as an inexcusable violation of human rights and the principles of social justice (Retsas, 1998; May, 2005).

May (2005) for example makes the case for a 'force free' mental health service, arguing that the use of restraint can leave people with resentment and mistrust of staff and care services. Restraint can also leave a deep and lasting effect on people's psychological and emotional well-being, denying people their dignity and damaging their self-respect.

Carlile (2006) argues that when restraints are premeditated they constitute punishment rather than an intervention to secure safety, and should therefore not be used. However, there will inevitably be some behaviours and situations that are so challenging that planning is required to deal with these situations. The Youth Justice Board (2006) argues that restraint use requires some forethought, as risk assessments and planning need to be put in place. These differences in opinion are also reflected in the small body of work that has examined the views of people who have been restrained (Morgan, 2004; CSCI, 2007). Some people who use services appreciate the need for either themselves or others to be restrained in some circumstances. CSCI (2007) illustrates a case when an older person was becoming violent and the sensitive use of restraint helped to calm the person down. Reflecting May's (2005) concerns, however, is the use of distraction techniques hours before the suicide of Adam Rickwood – the youngest death in a secure training centre in modern times – where these painful techniques clearly had a deep effect on him:

> When I calmed down I asked them why they hit me in the nose and jumped on me. They said it was because I wouldn't go in my room so I said what gives them the right to hit a 14-year-old child in the nose and they said it was restraint (letter by Adam Rickwood cited in Allison and Hattenstone, 2007).

Challenges for services

Blanket forms of restraint and restraint that is integrated into routine practice can rarely be justified. Such practices risk breaching people's human and civil rights. However, it is important to recognise that rarely will staff set out to deliberately mistreat or harm people. Rather, staff can find themselves in difficult situations whilst delivering care that may at times be intimate and intricate and at other times challenging and fast paced. Staff face tensions between respecting people's rights and freedoms to make choices and take risks, alongside the need to ensure that risks are managed and people are kept safe. These pressures to keep people safe have come from staff, people using services, their friends and relatives, and the general public.

There is clearly a need to acknowledge the climate of practice in different care settings. In addition, there are some core values that enable people's human rights to be maximised:

- respect for people's dignity
- respect for autonomy and self-reliance
- promotion of overall well-being
- promotion of fairness and equality

Respect and promotion of these values requires a philosophical shift to understand the meaning of individuals' behaviour and to ensure sensitive responses to people's needs, however expressed.

> If we spent as much time on trying to understand behaviour as we spend trying to manage or control it, we might discover that what lies behind it is a genuine attempt to communicate (Goldsmith, 2007).

Looking in detail at the circumstances that give rise to particular forms of behaviour is important to get beyond the surface of the issue and to better understand things from the perspective of the individual. This approach maximises opportunities for interventions that promote people's health and well-being. Staff therefore have professional responsibilities to understand the reasons for individuals' behaviour and to think about what effect any use of restraint might have on the person concerned.

There are a host of principles and guidelines that apply to the use of restraint across care settings. The purpose here is not to restate them but to draw out some of the key ethical dimensions.

- *Involvement.* People need to be involved in plans and decisions about the use of restraint, including their understanding of the benefits and risks associated with the restraint and its alternatives.
- *Awareness.* Restraint may take place in certain situations and in prescribed ways, and individuals need to be aware of this. They also need to be aware that restraint is taking place, which may not always happen in the case of covert medication or when people's mental capacity is impaired.
- *Control.* The degrees of control on the use of restraint and influence on when restraint can be stopped by the individual. The least practical amount of force or coercion should be used for the shortest time. Blanket forms of restraint, approaches that become ingrained into the routines of care provision and interventions that are more than short-term measures should never be used.
- *Intent.* Distinctions should be made clear between restraining actions that are intended to restrain and those that are unintentional consequences of other actions or activities.

■ *Motivation.* The underlying motives for using restraint should always be critically reviewed and questioned. Is the restraining action serving the individual's best interests and operating in a person-centred way?

Conclusions

Citizens who use health and social care services have the same rights as everybody else, unless their rights are limited by law. The use of restraint gets to the very heart of basic human and civil rights. Some forms of restraint are easily recognisable, but a broad typology is needed to understand the whole host of ways in which people's freedoms can be restrained. A broad framework is especially useful for exposing subtle forms of restraint and those practices that are restrictive but may be taken for granted in everyday practice.

There is a debate to be had about what restraint-free care involves, as there will undoubtedly be exceptional circumstances when some form of restraint or coercion is required. The examples of different forms of restraint illustrated in this chapter alert us to the need to take note of the broader social and organisational contexts in which restraint takes place. Sometimes staff will use restraints to help deal with managerial and organisational pressures and the use of restraint in these situations will not always be undertaken with the best interests of individuals in mind. Staff are faced with difficult dilemmas around support and care, notably enabling people to make their own choices and take appropriate risks and balancing these with care and safety considerations. Clearly, there are tensions in practice when staff are left to deal with these dilemmas alone and without sufficient education, training and support. High-quality health and social care is all about putting people first, providing truly personalised services and treating people with maximum dignity and respect. To deliver these services in ways that keep the use of restraints to an absolute minimum requires the right working conditions and resources to enable staff to provide the highest quality care.

References

All Party Parliamentary Group on Dementia (2008) *Minutes of Proceedings at a Parliamentary Hearing on Use of Antipsychotic Drugs in Residential Care Homes Held in Committee Room 13, House of Commons on Monday 4 February 2008.* From the shorthand notes of WB Gurney & Sons LLP.

Allison, E. and Hattenstone, S. (2007) What gives them the right to hit a child in the nose? *The Guardian*, 2 June 2007. http://www.guardian.co.uk/society/2007/jun/02/youthjustice.politics (accessed 1 March 2009).

Alzheimer's Society (2007) *Safer Walking Technology.* Alzheimer's Society, London.

Ball, H. N. (2005) Deaths from restraints: lessons. *Psychiatric Bulletin*, **29**(9), 321–3.

British Institute of Human Rights (2007) *The Human Rights Act – Changing Lives.* London, British Institute of Human Rights.

Carlile of Berriew, Lord (2006) *An Independent Inquiry Into the Use of Physical Restraint, Solitary Confinement and Forcible Strip Searching of Children in Prisons, Secure Training Centres and Local Authority Secure Children's Homes.* Howard League for Penal Reform, London.

Carney, T., Tait, D., Richardson, A. and Touyz, S. (2008) Why (and when) clinicians compel treatment of anorexia nervosa patients. *European Eating Disorders Review*, **16**(3), 199–206.

Commission for Social Care Inspection (CSCI) (2007) *Rights, Risks and Restraints. An Exploration Into the Use of Restraint in the Care of Older People.* Commission for Social Care Inspection, London.

Commission for Social Care Inspection (CSCI) (2008) *See Me, Not Just the Dementia. Understanding People's Experiences of Living in a Care Home.* Commission for Social Care Inspection, London.

Department for Children, Schools and Families (2007) *The Use of Force to Control or Restrain Pupils. Non Statutory Guidance for Schools in England.* Department for Children, Schools and Families, London.

Department of Health (DH) (2007) *Human Rights in Healthcare – A Framework for Local Action.* DH, London.

Economic and Social Research Council (2007) *Human Rights, a Tool for Change.* Economic and Social Research Council, Swindon.

Goldsmith, M. (1996) Slow down and listen to their voice. *Journal of Dementia Care*, **4**(4), 24–5.

Harris, J., Cornick, M., Jefferson, A. and Mills, R. (2008) *Physical Interventions: a Policy Framework*, 2nd edn. British Institute of Learning Disabilities, Kidderminster.

Hart, D. and Howell, S. (2004) *Report on the Use of Physical Intervention across Children's Services.* National Children's Bureau, London.

Healthcare Commission and Commission for Social Care Inspection (2006) *Joint Investigation into the Provision of Services for People with Learning Disabilities at Cornwall Partnership NHS Trust.* Healthcare Commission, London.

Healthcare Commission (2007a) *Investigation into the Service for People with Learning Disabilities Provided by Sutton and Merton Primary Care Trust.* Healthcare Commission, London.

Healthcare Commission (2007b) *A Life Like no Other: a National Audit of Specialist Inpatient Healthcare Services for People with Learning Difficulties in England.* Healthcare Commission, London.

Horsburgh, D., Rowat, A., Mahoney, C. and Dennis, M. (2008) A necessary evil? Interventions to prevent nasogastric tube-tugging after stroke. *British Journal of Neuroscience Nursing*, **4**(5), 230–4.

House of Commons Health Committee (2004) *Elder Abuse. Second Report of Session 2003–04. Volume 1. Report, together with formal minutes.* Stationery Office, London.

Hughes, J. C. and Louw, S. J. (2002) Electronic tagging of people with dementia who wander. *BMJ,* **325**(7369), 847–8.

Irving, K. (2002) Governing the conduct of conduct: are restraints inevitable? *Journal of Advanced Nursing,* **40**(4), 405–12.

May, R. (2005) Compassion not compulsion. *Psychminded.* http://www.psychminded. co.uk/news/news2005/feb05/rufusmaycolumn.htm (accessed 1 March 2009).

Mental Welfare Commission for Scotland (2007) *The Use of Seclusion. Guidance on Good Practice.* Mental Welfare Commission for Scotland, Edinburgh.

Morgan, R. (2004) *Children's Views on Restraint. The Views of Children and Young People in Residential Homes and Residential Special Schools.* Office of the Children's Rights Director, Newcastle.

Mott, S., Poole, J. and Kenrick, M. (2005) Physical and chemical restraints in acute care: their potential impact on the rehabilitation of older people. *International Journal of Nursing Practice,* **11**(3), 95–101.

Paterson, B., Bradley, P., Stark, C., Saddled, D., Leadbetter, D. and Allen, D. (2003) Deaths associated with restraint use in health and social care in the UK. The results of a preliminary survey. *Journal of Psychiatric and Mental Health Nursing,* **10**(1), 3–15.

Retsas, A. P. (1998) Survey findings describing the use of physical restraint in nursing homes in Victoria, Australia. *International Journal of Nursing Studies,* **35**(3), 184–91.

UK Children's Commissioners (2008) *Report to the UN Committee on the Rights of the Child.* UK Children's Commissioners, London.

United Nations (UN) (2002). *Committee on the Rights of the Child. Thirty-first session. Consideration of reports submitted by state parties under article 44 of the convention. Concluding observations: United Kingdom and Northern Ireland.* United Nations, Geneva.

Welsh, S., Hassiotis, A., O'Mahoney, G. and Deahl, M. (2003) Big brother is watching you – the ethical implications of electronic surveillance measures in the elderly with dementia and in adults with learning difficulties. *Aging and Mental Health,* **7**(5), 372–5.

Youth Justice Board (2006) *A Response to Lord Carlile's Inquiry into Children in Custody.* Youth Justice Board, London.

CHAPTER 3

The physical restraint of children and young people

Di Hart

Introduction

This chapter considers the use of restraint on children and young people under the age of 18, referred to as children to reflect their legal status. Children are particularly vulnerable to being forced to comply with adult wishes because of the imbalance in their strength and authority. Physical restraint is one way in which this superior power may be exercised and is a particularly topical issue at the time of writing following the restraint related deaths of two teenagers in secure training centres (STCs) for young offenders. Gareth Myatt died in 2004 after being held in a 'seated double embrace' (SDE) hold that restricted his airway, and later in the same year Adam Rickwood committed suicide. His distress and anger about an incident of physical restraint earlier in the day were thought to have been contributory factors.

It is important to remember that the practice of restraint is not limited to youth justice settings: children in residential or foster care, schools, hospitals and immigration centres may be restrained, as may children within their own family. Restraint is a normal and unquestioned element of care for young children: a parent who did not grab a toddler heading for a busy road would be negligent and failing in their duty of care. Ethical considerations about the undesirability of overpowering a child must be weighed against risk assessments of the harmful consequences of not doing so.

When consulted, children recognise that restraint can be legitimate and are not calling for it to be prohibited. They want it to be 'done properly', meaning only when the circumstances genuinely warrant it and without the use of excessive force. Safeguards are therefore needed to make sure that this is the case.

This chapter will explore:

- the legal and policy framework for the use of restraint on children
- the methods of restraint that are used
- the nature of the evidence base
- how restraint can be reduced
- the need to improve safeguards

Legal and policy framework

There is no single set of criteria determining the circumstances when restraint can be used on children. In fact, the legal and policy framework is contradictory: behaviour that could lawfully result in physical restraint in a school would not present sufficient legal justification in a children's home. This can be particularly problematic for staff working in residential schools, where both sets of legislation apply. There have been previous calls for a review of the use of restraint on children. In 2002, the Committee responsible for monitoring compliance with the *United Nations (UN) Convention on the Rights of the Child* (2002) suggested that the UK may be in breach through its frequent use of restraint in residential institutions and in custody. This concern was echoed in the Joint Chief Inspectors' report on safeguarding in 2005 (Commission for Social Care Inspection (CSCI), 2005) which called upon government to: 'Issue one agreed set of principles for the use of control methods in all settings where children are cared for, including secure settings'. This was accepted in principle but has not been implemented.

What are the criteria for the use of restraint in the absence of such a set of principles? Many services do not distinguish between children and adults when it comes to guidance on the use of restraint. The following are the criteria for restraint in the settings where it is more likely to be used, although incidence data is sadly lacking.

Children's homes

The legal framework for the use of physical restraint in all children's homes is that:

> ... restraint should be used rarely and only to prevent a child harming himself or others or from damaging property. Force should not be

used for any other purpose, nor simply to secure compliance with staff instructions (Department of Health (DH), 1991).

Subsequently, there was some concern that staff were interpreting the criteria too narrowly and felt, for example, unable to prevent a vulnerable child from running away even when they would be at risk. In 1997 the Chief Inspector of the Social Services Inspectorate issued a letter emphasising that staff have a duty of care to intervene to prevent children from harming themselves or others, or seriously damaging property and that they should '... interpret 'harm' widely and ... anticipate when it is clearly likely to happen' (DH, 2003). Moreover, it is the *action* that needs to be immediate – not the *risk*:

> ... if necessary staff have the authority to take immediate action to prevent harm occurring even if the harm is expected to happen some time in the predictable future (DH, 2003).

Secure settings

Children may have their liberty restricted either through the youth justice system or for 'welfare' reasons under section 25 of the Children Act 1989. There are three types of secure establishment: young offender institutions (YOIs) run by the prison service; STCs run by private contractors; and secure children's homes. In spite of their very similar populations, the criteria for using restraint are different in all three. Secure children's homes are expected to comply with the legal framework for other types of children's homes, but with the additional power to restrain a child who attempts to escape. YOIs are bound by the same rules as adult prisons and operate within a less restrictive set of criteria. Although prison officers are instructed not to use force unless it is necessary, this is not clearly explained. Instead of the risk-based model described above there is reference to the use of force to control 'violent, refractory or disturbed behaviour' (Prison Service Order 1600).

The circumstances in which physical restraint can be used in STCs are set out in the STC Rules as follows:

> No trainee shall be physically restrained save where necessary for the purpose of preventing him/her from:
>
> - escape from custody;
> - injuring themselves or others;
> - damaging property; or

- inciting another trainee to do anything specified in paragraph (b) or (c) above, and then only where no alternative method of preventing the event specified in any of paragraphs (a) to (d) above is available.

These criteria are based on the same conceptual framework as those for children's homes: that of 'risk' rather than 'recalcitrance'. It is not enough for the child's behaviour to be challenging: it must also be likely to lead to harmful consequences if not checked. These rules were amended by the Youth Justice Board (YJB) in June 2007 to authorise the use of restraint if there was a threat to 'good order and discipline'. A subsequent appeal in July 2008 deemed that this change had been unlawful and it has been withdrawn (*R[C]* v. *The Secretary for State for Justice in the Court of Appeal and the Divisional Court*). The controversy over the rule change and the two recent deaths prompted government to undertake a review of restraint in juvenile secure settings.

Education

The Education and Inspections Act 2006 provides the legislative basis for the use of force to control or restrain pupils within schools. Section 93 enables school staff:

> ... to use such force as is reasonable in the circumstances to prevent a pupil from doing, or continuing to do, any of the following:
>
> a) committing an offence
> b) causing personal injury or damage to the property of any person (including the pupil himself); or
> c) prejudicing the maintenance of good order and discipline at the school or among any pupils receiving education at the school, whether during a teaching session or otherwise.

Section 95 gives the head teacher authority to decide which paid and unpaid staff can use these powers, including catering or premise-related staff. Additional guidance has been provided in *The Use of Force to Control or Restrain Pupils* (Department for Children, Schools and Families (DCSF), 2007) and there is more detailed guidance in relation to pupils with severe behavioural difficulties, primarily in special school settings (Department for Education and Skills, 2003).

The Use of Force to Control or Restrain Pupils states that there is no legal definition of when it is reasonable to use force but that it will always depend on the circumstances. While it is not justifiable to use restraint for instances of 'trivial misbehaviour', the interpretation of this will vary. An example is given that a child running in a corridor crowded with small children may justify the use of restraint.

Health

There is no statutory guidance specifically on the restraint on children in health settings, although the new guidelines to be developed for those in psychiatric hospital by the Care Services Improvement Partnership and the National Institute of Mental Health in England will include a section on children. Good practice guidelines have, however, been issued by the Royal College of Nursing (RCN, 2003). Nurses may need to hold children during unpleasant clinical procedures, as well as in the situations of challenging behaviour normally associated with restraint, and the guidelines are based on the need to respect the child's rights. Wherever possible, the need to hold a child should be agreed in advance with the child and the parents, and the RCN is calling for an audit of the use of restraint.

Interpreting the criteria

Whatever the 'rules' about the justification for using restraint, they must be interpreted by practitioners in relation to individual children in real-life situations. Most of these will be in the context of a crisis, with little opportunity to seek advice. Guidance documents tend to contain general principles rather than specific instruction. For example, most indicate that restraint should be a last resort, justifiable only to prevent harm rather than to punish or secure compliance, and the degree of force should be minimal, reasonable and proportionate. What does this mean in practice? One person's understanding of what constitutes a last resort may be very different from another's. The evidence to the Joint Committee on Human Rights (2008) illustrated the complexity of these judgements. An example was given where a group of boys refusing to go to bed could jeopardise the 'good order and discipline' of an establishment and staff would be justified in using restraint because of the potential consequences if staff lost control. This argument was not accepted by the Committee.

In spite of the search for certainty, judgements will always be subjective and it is evident that different staff groups, or individuals within the group, have different thresholds for using restraint. This is illustrated by the varying levels of restraint in different establishments dealing with essentially the same types of children, but is also recognised in the following quote from a residential worker:

> One person that I do know uses restraint in very, kind of, in the kids' faces (Steckley and Kendrick, 2005).

Even where the criteria have been met, in that a child has been restrained because they were behaving aggressively, the challenge is to look at the context in which the incident took place. It is important to acknowledge the dynamic nature of the interactions between children and the adults caring for them: it is not just the child's behaviour that is of interest if an incident is to be understood. What happened to make the child behave in that way? And could the adults have responded differently? Is the ethos of the establishment such that restraint is an unquestioned part of day-to-day life or seen as an opportunity to reflect on ways of improving practice?

> Staff rile you until you want to hit them, then they restrain you (young person cited in Morgan, 2004).

If the use of restraint is to be reduced, there must be an awareness that the use of restraint can become institutionalised. This theme will be revisited later in the chapter.

Methods of restraint

Just as there is no consistency across children's services about the circumstances in which restraint can be used, there is no consistency about the techniques that are sanctioned. Managers of children's homes are told only that they must select methods of restraint that are suitable for use on children and to provide training for their staff. This presents them with a challenge: how are they meant to know which methods are safe and suitable in the absence of any mandatory system of accreditation? Local authorities and children's home providers have chosen a wide range of methods from within the commercial sector. The same applies to education settings, where guidance is even more vague and where decisions about training are left to the discretion of individual schools.

In contrast, YOIs and STCs have prescribed methods that must be used. The prison service has adopted 'control and restraint' (C&R) within all its establishments, regardless of the age of those detained. It relies on 'pain compliant' techniques; that is to say ways of holding the person that will cause pain if they resist. These put pressure across the joints through, for example, wrist locks and arm locks. The method devised specifically for STCs is Physical Control in Care (PCC) and is not reliant on pain compliance. Instead it consists of a series of holds designed to restrict the young person's movement. The holds are phased according to the seriousness of the situation. The death of Gareth Myatt prompted questions about how this method, said to be medically approved, could have caused asphyxiation. The government review of restraint in secure settings is considering the safety of the techniques currently in use, and a number of holds have been banned in the interim.

It is not just the safety of methods that has been questioned: considerable attention has been paid to the ethical validity of the deliberate application of pain. PCC, and other methods that have received less publicity, contain some 'distraction' techniques that have been particularly controversial. These deliver a short episode of pain in extreme situations where the normal holds cannot be applied because, for example, the child has a weapon. Adam Rickwood had been the subject of a 'nose distraction' the day he died that had made his nose bleed. This technique has subsequently been suspended.

In fact, there is considerable uncertainty at the moment about what can and cannot be done. Various techniques have been suspended and a letter has gone out from the DCSF to secure children's homes raising doubts about the safety of methods that take children to the floor. Staff would welcome more explicit guidance on the methods that *are* suitable as well as restrictions on those that are not.

The evidence base

There are risks inherent in any type of physical restraint. The most obvious of these may be the risk of physical harm: whilst deaths are rare, children sustain fractures or other injuries including grazes, bruising and carpet burns. Staff also sustain injuries, and their fitness for work may be affected in the short or longer term. More intangible, but arguably equally damaging, are the emotional and psychological consequences of restraint. Again, these may affect both staff and young people. Given the importance of these issues, it is surprising that so little research has been done on the safety, effectiveness and impact of restraint in the UK and even less on the specific issues relating to children. More studies have been undertaken in the USA, but the findings are not all transferable to other countries where services are very different. A useful review of the literature was undertaken for the Wales Office in which the authors concluded:

There is very little scientifically robust research on the use of physical restraint with children, methods of restraint that are safe for use with children, training effectiveness, or comparisons of different training methods. This lack of knowledge contributes to government reluctance to set clear guidelines, the difficulty for service providers in selecting appropriate training, and the development of systems of accreditation for training providers (Hughes *et al.*, 2001).

Safety and effectiveness

Most research into the safety and effectiveness of restraint techniques is on the use of C&R in adult health settings. Studies that have focused on children are scarce, in spite of a recognition that children's bones may be more susceptible to injury. A study that looked at 45 fatalities of children in residential care in the USA found that 25 were caused by asphyxia and that, in 23 instances, the criteria for the legitimate use of restraint did not appear to have been met (Nunno *et al.*, 2006). Some individual training providers, such as Crisis, Aggression, Limitation and Management (CALM) and TeamTeach, ask establishments using their methods to submit reports on the incidence of injuries associated with particular techniques in an attempt to build an evidence base, but there is no systematic attempt to collect and analyse data across methods in the UK. The YJB has recently established a reporting system for the secure settings in which they place children, but data are limited and there is no equivalent system for social care or health settings.

Research is difficult to do, however. A particular technique is only as good as the people using it. Where injury has been caused, it must be established whether the hold was applied correctly, and this is very difficult to achieve in a real-life crisis situation. Issues of skill and training are also part of the equation. Killick and Allen (2005) found that confidence in dealing with violent situations was improved immediately after training, but not maintained. Bell and Stark (1998) studied the factors involved in assessing competence in physical restraint skills and noted the difficulty in acquiring and retaining skills through training courses. They concluded that there was a need for a high level of practice during training, frequent refresher training and effective monitoring and assessment of practice. Even in 'laboratory' conditions observers found it difficult to judge whether a given method of restraint was being applied correctly.

It is clear that ways of evaluating methods must be found, however. In the absence of evidence, practice is driven by assumptions and moral positioning. The British Institute of Learning Disabilities (BILD) is in the process of developing a rating tool that is designed to critically analyse techniques in terms of their safety, effectiveness and social validity. It is essential that all three elements are considered. A technique may be safe and ethical, in that it does not inflict pain, but if it does not work and someone is badly hurt as a result it is hard to see how it can be justified. Conversely, a reliance on a pain-compliant technique may be effective but provoke such humiliation and rage that the child can no longer engage in trusting relationships with adults. It is not only the immediate and short-term effects that are relevant, but the long-term impact on health and well-being.

Impact studies

There have been a number of recent studies in the UK gathering the views of those most directly involved: children and front-line staff. Most have focused on children in the care system. In the Lindsay and Hosie (2000) study of children's homes in Edinburgh, 68 per cent of the children reported that they had been the subject of restraint and 44 per cent had experienced prone restraint; that is to say where they had been held down on the floor. Interestingly, not all the children's comments were negative and complaints were more likely to be made about the fact that restraint had been used unfairly than the fact that it had been used at all. Other consultations with looked after children confirm these mixed reactions (Who Cares? Scotland, 2003; Morgan, 2004; Steckley and Kendrick, 2005). Children were left feeling angry if they believed that restraint was used unfairly, applied incorrectly or using excessive force. The range of negative views included:

- experiences of pain and injury
- perceiving restraint as a punishment
- feeling abused or violated
- negative impact on relationship with staff
- lack of opportunity to debrief and make sense of the incident
- disempowerment

The perception that restraint was used as a punishment was in spite of the official justification given and some children were left with a real sense of grievance that adults could do what they liked and there was no point in complaining. This was particularly difficult for children who had been removed from their family because of abuse and then felt further abused by carers.

Children were also confused about which restraint techniques were 'right' and which were 'wrong', particularly those who had experienced multiple placements where different techniques may have been used. Adverse reactions were particularly pervasive if the child had no opportunity to discuss what had happened so that they could make sense of it or put their own perspective. A consultation exercise with children exclusively within secure settings was particularly negative (Carlile, 2006), with children describing experiences of rough handling and verbal abuse during restraint incidents. Concerns were also raised about the circumstances where restraint was used, with examples given of children being restrained for refusing to go to another classroom or to their room, or following provocation by staff.

It is important to note that children in other reports are able to report instances where the use of restraint had been reassuring and a demonstration that staff cared enough to keep them safe from harm.

> If a restraint that's getting done on me is done correctly then I feel safe because they're stopping me from hurting myself, hurting somebody else or doing something stupid (Who Cares? Scotland, 2003).

Staff in children's homes also describe a similar range of complex emotions (Bell, 1997; Lindsay and Hosie, 2000; Steckley and Kendrick, 2005). Some struggle to reconcile the use of restraint with their commitment to empowering and nurturing children. Other concerns include:

■ lack of confidence in their ability to apply the restraint techniques, particularly if they have received inadequate training or do not have faith in the method
■ concern about the possibility of physical or psychological harm to the child
■ recognition of the need for better care planning
■ worry about the impact on their relationship with the child
■ fear of litigation or complaint – and the extent to which they will receive support from management
■ lack of clarity about the guidance
■ insufficient opportunities for debriefing

As with the young people, opportunities to offload, reflect and learn from incidents were considered to be valuable. The Scottish Institute for Residential Child Care (SIRCC, 2005) has produced comprehensive guidance to support children's homes in developing their practice.

Reducing the use of restraint

Perhaps the key to improving practice is to focus not on when and how restraint can be used, but on how it can be avoided. There are two ways of approaching this:

- individualised behaviour management
- changing organisational culture.

These are not mutually exclusive and the use of restraint is most likely to be reduced if a twin-track approach is adopted.

Behaviour management

An approach that treats all children (and staff) as being the same and tries to present a simple formula (behaviour A = restraint technique B) is unhelpful and contributes to the institutionalisation of restraint. The focus should rather be on a perception that challenging behaviour is a means of communicating personal distress and that it deserves to be responded to as such.

> It is not uncommon in some settings to encounter descriptions of children's violent behaviours as 'acting up', 'acting out' or 'kicking off'. The use of such terms provides a barrier for staff allowing them to maintain an emotional distance from the actual emotions of the child whether of anger, fear and loss (Paterson *et al.*, 2008, p. 34).

If risky or problematic behaviour is to be managed, it must first be understood. Testing-out behaviour is a normal part of childhood and adolescence. For those dealing with additional challenges, particularly if they are living away from home, the urge towards self-harm or aggression may well be exaggerated by fear and anxiety. It could be argued that the worst thing to do to children in these circumstances is to accommodate them with other children with behavioural difficulties but this is exactly what happens within children's homes, custodial settings and hospitals.

Every child has their own strengths and vulnerabilities. A child with autistic spectrum disorder is likely to be overwhelmed in a group and may lash out if it gets too much to bear, whereas a child who has been abused may fear being alone and resort to self-harm. These differences need to be recognised and reflected in the way the behaviour is managed. The best approach to risky behaviour is to prevent it from arising, and each child should have their own behaviour management plan to which they, parents, social workers and carers have contributed. This will identify the triggers that cause the child distress, the early warning signs that all is not well and ways in which staff can help reduce the stress. If it is thought that physical restraint may have a part to play, the ways in which this will be done can be discussed. Risks associated with the child's physical or emotional health, or personal preferences, can be identified so that the most suitable methods are agreed in advance.

This individualised risk assessment and response needs to be dynamic rather than cast in stone. The plan should be revisited after each incident so that lessons can be learned and the plan updated. It should also link to the overall care plan for the child: maybe the child needs more support than the establishment can provide? The need for this holistic approach has been recognised within the National Minimum Standards for children in regulated settings (DH, 2002) which requires them to have a behaviour management policy within which the use of restraint plays a small part. The good practice guidelines produced by the Secure Accommodation Network (SAN, 2005) and the YJB code of conduct on behaviour management (YJB, 2006) support this holistic position. They describe the arrangements that should be in place before, during and after restraint, including the expectation that crises will be defused wherever possible.

Diversion, defusion and de-escalation strategies are an important element in behaviour management. Effective training must include these as an integral part of the strategies they offer and there are methods of intervention that focus specifically on these such as Therapeutic Crisis Intervention (TCI).

A positive culture

There is increasing awareness that challenging behaviour can be reduced if there is a real commitment within an establishment to doing so. Recognising that practice guidance and training are not sufficient to bring about change, the SIRCC with the Care Commission hosted a recent leadership seminar to look at continuing concerns about restraint practice in Scotland (SIRCC, 2007). They identified the priority as being the creation of a positive culture of care.

Leadbetter criticises the notion that training in conflict management is the only response to challenging behaviour.

> Such responses effectively 'individualise' the problem and reinforce blame cultures, obscuring the link between service quality and assault rates. They rarely produce positive outcomes and often increase risk (Leadbetter, 2007).

Blame may be attributed to individuals for behaving in the way they do, or to staff for having insufficient skills to deal with them. Either way, the organisation itself does not have to take ownership of the problem. The consultations with children and staff described earlier, and the current debate on 'good order and discipline' suggest that there may be more to it than that. Paterson *et al.* (2008) refer to the dynamic within 'toxic' organisations characterised by a culture of shame and humiliation amongst staff and users. Within this culture, there is an expectation of submissiveness, and interactions with others are seen as potentially threatening. A positive culture of care starts with a recognition that the organisation has work to do and sets a goal to reduce not just the use of restraint but the need for it.

A restraint reduction strategy will need to be multifaceted. Paterson *et al.* (2008) suggest that change begins with the articulation of a vision statement, but supported by a project management approach that sets objectives, such as a 50 per cent reduction in restraint levels and a timetable for delivering them. Initiatives are then put into place that will achieve these objectives. For example, it might be decided that senior management will attend after every episode of restraint. Whatever local objectives are set, there will need to be a virtuous circle of reflection to assess progress and agree what remains to be done. Attention may need to be focused on anything from the physical environment (are there hot spots where conflict is more likely to take place?) to less tangible factors (do staff treat each other with respect?). The 'atmosphere' of an establishment conveys an important message and a review of 'what works' in children's residential care suggested the strategic, leadership and practice elements that may contribute (Clough *et al.*, 2006). Colton (2004) has developed an audit tool that can be used to determine whether an organisation is ready to reduce seclusion and restraint.

The importance of monitoring has also been highlighted by research (Deveau and McGill, 2007) and is confirmed in discussion with managers. Some have described how the decision to review all incidents of restraint has in itself been enough to bring about a reduction. More sophisticated analyses of where incidents have taken place, who has been involved, what the triggers were and the attempts made to defuse the situation enable improvements in practice, both for the individuals involved and the organisation as a whole. Many services have developed systems for undertaking this analysis but arrangements for independent external monitoring are patchy. There is also a lack of national data about the incidence of restraint on children, weakening the ability to apply rigorous independent monitoring.

Conclusion

Practitioners that say they will never restrain children because they do not want to harm them may produce the opposite effect and the children may see them as indifferent to their safety. On the other hand, there is clearly no room for complacency about the way that restraint is currently being practised. The UK Children's Commissioners' report to the UN Committee on the Rights of the Child (2008) questions the government assertion that restraint is only used as a last resort and calls for methods that cause pain to be banned. The latest

Joint Chief Inspectors report on safeguarding (Office for Standards in Education, Children's Services and Skills, 2008) also concluded that all is not well and has recommended that the government provide guidance on the behaviour management of children and young people, emphasising that restraint should not be used solely to gain compliance and that methods of restraint should not rely on pain compliance, and that injuries caused by restraint in custodial settings should be monitored by the Local Safeguarding Children Board.

The exercise of power must always be taken seriously and constantly questioned. It is suggested that additional safeguards are needed to ensure children's safety:

- Clear and consistent guidance across children's services about the situations where restraint is justified.
- A national, independent and mandatory accreditation system for restraint methods and training.
- Research on the safety, effectiveness and emotional impact of restraint on children and staff, and on the different restraint methods.
- A debate about the meaning of best practice in relation to behaviour management and restraint leading to national principles or standards.
- A more robust system for the monitoring of restraint by independent people with appropriate expertise.
- A national system of data collection and analysis, including the incidence of restraint and injuries caused.
- An expectation that all organisations have a restraint reduction policy, setting out the changes they intend to make in order to bring down their incidence of restraint.

As Utting (1997) reminded us restraint can easily tip over into abuse.

References

Bell, L. (1997) The physical restraint of young people. *Child and Family Social Work*, 2(1), 37–47.

Bell, L. and Stark, C. (1998) *Measuring Competence in Physical Restraint Skills in Residential Child Care*. Scottish Office Central Research Unit, Edinburgh.

Carlile of Berriew, Lord (2006) *An Independent Inquiry Into the Use of Physical Restraint, Solitary Confinement and Forcible Strip Searching of Children in Prisons, Secure Training Centres and Local Authority Secure Children's Homes*. Howard League for Penal Reform, London.

Clough, R., Bullock, R. and Ward, A. (2006) *What Works in Residential Child Care: a Review of Research Evidence and the Practical Consideration*. National Children's Bureau, London

Colton, D. (2004) *Checklist for Assessing Your Organization's Readiness for Reducing Seclusion and Restraint*. Commonwealth Center for Children and Adolescents, Staunton, VA.

Commission for Social Care Inspection (CSCI) (2005) *Safeguarding Children: the Second Joint Chief Inspectors' Report on Arrangements to Safeguard Children*. CSCI, London.

Department for Education and Skills (2003) *Guidance on the Use of Restrictive Physical Interventions or Pupils with Severe Behavioural Difficulties*. Department for Education and Skills, London.

Department for Children, Schools and Families (2007) *The Use of Force to Control or Restrain Pupils. Non Statutory Guidance for Schools in England*. Department for Children, Schools and Families, London.

Department of Health (DH) (1991) *The Children Act 1989 Guidance and Regulations. Volume 4: Residential Care*. Her Majesty's Stationery Office, London.

Department of Health (DH) (1993) *Guidance on Permissible Forms of Control in Children's Residential Care*. DH, London.

Department of Health (DH) (1997) *The Control of Children in the Public Care: Interpretation of the Children Act 1989. (CI(97)6)*. DH, London.

Department of Health (DH) (2002) *Children's Homes. National Minimum Standards. Children's Homes Regulations*. DH, London.

Deveau, R. and McGill, P. (2007) *As the Last Resort: Reducing the Use of Restrictive Physical Interventions*. University of Kent, Canterbury.

Hart, D. (2004) *Report on the Use of Physical Intervention Across Children's Services*. National Children's Bureau, London.

Hart, D. and Howell, S. (2003) *Report to the Youth Justice Board on the use of Physical Intervention within the Juvenile Secure Estate*. YJB, London.

Hughes, J. C., Hutchings, J., Berry, H. E., Allen, D., Ingram, E. and Tilley, E. F. (2001) *A Review of Literature Relating to Safe Forms of Restraint for Children with Behaviour That is Difficult to Manage*. Wales Office of Research and Development, Cardiff.

Joint Committee on Human Rights (2008) *The Use of Restraint in Secure Training Centres. HL Paper 65. HC 378*. Stationery Office, London.

Killick, S. and Allen, D. (2005) Training staff in an adolescent inpatient psychiatric unit in positive approaches to managing aggressive and harmful behaviour: does it improve confidence and knowledge? *Child Care in Practice*, **11**(3), 323–39.

Leadbetter, D. (2007) With strong leadership we can improve the use of restraint. *Community Care*, 4 October, p. 21.

Lindsay, M. and Hosie, A. (2000) *The Edinburgh Inquiry – Recommendation 55. The Independent Evaluation Report*. University of Strathclyde and Centre for Residential Child Care, Glasgow.

Morgan, R. (2004) *Children's Views on Restraint. The Views of Children and Young People in Residential Homes and Residential Special Schools*. Office of the Children's Rights Director, Newcastle.

Nunno, M., Holden, J. and Tollar, A. (2006) Learning from tragedy: a survey of child and adolescent restraint fatalities. *Child Abuse and Neglect*, **30**(12), 1329–31.

Office for Standards in Education, Children's Services and Skills (Ofsted) (2008) *Safeguarding Children: the Third Joint Chief Inspectors' Report on Arrangements to Safeguard Children*. Ofsted, London.

Paterson, B., Leadbetter, D., Miller, G. and Crichton, J. (2008) Adopting a public health model to reduce violence and restraints in children's residential care facilities. In: *For Our Own Safety: Examining the Safety of High Risk Interventions for Children and Young People* (eds. M. A. Nunno, D. M. Day and L. B. Bullard), Child Welfare League of America, Washington, DC.

Prison Service Order 1600 *The Use of Force*.

Royal College of Nursing (2003) *Restraining, Holding Still and Containing Children and Young People: Guidance for Nursing Staff*. RCN, London

Scottish Institute for Residential Child Care (SIRCC) (2005) *Holding Safely: a Guide for Residential Child Care Practitioners and Managers about Physically Restraining Children and Young People*. SIRCC, Glasgow.

Scottish Institute for Residential Child Care (SIRCC) (2007) *Physical Restraint: a Culture Shift for Organisations? Leadership Seminar Report and Recommendations*. SIRCC, Glasgow.

Secure Accommodation Network (SAN) (2005) *The Use of Restrictive Physical Interventions (RPI) in Secure Children's Homes (England and Wales): Good Practice Guidance*. SAN, London.

Steckley, L. and Kendrick, A. (2005) *Physical Restraint in Residential Child Care: The Experiences of Young People and Residential Workers* (Conference Paper to 'Children and Youth in Emerging and Transforming Societies Conference', Oslo, 29 June – 3 July).

UK Children's Commissioners (2008) *UK Children's Commissioners' Report to the UN Committee on the Rights of the Child*. UK Children's Commissioners, London.

United Nations Committee on the Rights of the Child (2002) *Consideration of Reports Submitted by States Parties Under Article 44 of the Convention. Concluding Observations of the Committee on the Rights of the Child: United Kingdom of Great Britain and Northern Ireland*. United Nations, Geneva.

Utting, W. (1997) *People Like Us: The Report of the Review of the Safeguards for Children Living Away from Home*. Department of Health and Welsh Office, London.

Who Cares? Scotland (2003) *Let's Face It! Care 2003: Young People Tell Us How It Is*. Who Cares? Scotland, Glasgow.

Youth Justice Board (YJB) (2006) *Managing the Behaviour of Children and Young People in the Secure Estate: a Code of Conduct*. YJB, London.

CHAPTER 4

Physical restraint and adults with learning disabilities

John Turnbull and Debbie Townsend

Introduction

People with learning disabilities are one of the most vulnerable groups in society. Therefore the use of any physical intervention for this group inevitably raises ethical, legal and professional issues, especially where this intervention is aimed at restraining them. The past decade has seen a steady growth in studies and papers on the use of restraint for people with learning disabilities. This is due to a number of factors that include Government policies aimed at promoting the rights of people with learning disabilities (Department of Health (DH), 2001, 2009), an increased emphasis on regulation within public services, new models of service provision for people with learning disabilities, especially in specialist health services (DH, 2007) and, unfortunately, evidence showing that abuse of people in services is continuing (Healthcare Commission and Commission for Social Care Inspection (CSCI), 2006) in spite of reports, inquiries and Government action in this area.

This chapter offers a timely opportunity to explore the use of restraint and its alternatives in services for adults with learning disabilities. Given that the scope of services for people with learning disabilities is now very broad, the discussion will focus on services for people whose behaviour challenges services by being violent, aggressive or self-injurious. It will propose that services need to work simultaneously on three strategies to ensure that restraint is minimised. Firstly, there needs to be a managed approach to reduce any risks to the person and staff and to confine the use of restraint to specific conditions. Secondly, it will propose that services need to pay greater attention to the use of ecological methods to prevent situations arising in which people may need to be restrained. Thirdly it will propose that alternatives to restraint should be employed in areas where their use can be strictly monitored and evaluated. In particular, the chapter will:

- describe the circumstances under which people may need to be restrained
- describe and evaluate alternatives to restraint
- describe how staff can manage risks associated with restraint
- identify therapeutic and ecological factors that can reduce the need for restraint

What is a learning disability?

People with learning disabilities have a significantly reduced ability to understand new or complex information or learn new skills. They also have a reduced ability to cope independently or to function appropriately in social situations (Emerson *et al.*, 2001a). It is estimated that 2 per cent of the general population will have a learning disability, although the majority of people will have little need to contact specialist services for help and support. Around 0.4 per cent of the general population will have more severe learning disabilities. These people are more likely to need 24-hour support, will have one or more long term health conditions, such as epilepsy, motor impairment or a sensory impairment (McLaren and Bryson, 1987; Office of Population Censuses and Surveys, 1989) and many will be unable to use speech to express their needs. Amongst other people who may need the support of specialist services are those with mental health needs or people who have offending backgrounds and have been detained under the Mental Health Act. Many of these will have mild or moderate learning disabilities, but they will need the specialist knowledge of learning disability staff to deliver therapy and help them cope more successfully.

Of particular relevance when discussing the use of physical interventions is the concept of challenging behaviour. Challenging behaviour has been extensively described by Emerson (1995) but refers to behaviours such as violence and aggression, self-harm, self-stimulatory behaviour, hyperactivity and severe withdrawal. It is a term that is not confined to the field of learning disability, though up to 15 per cent of all people in contact with services have been described as displaying one or more types of challenging behaviour (Emerson *et al*, 2001b). The origins of challenging behaviour are several. However, for people with learning disabilities, their intellectual and physical impairments make it likely they will use behaviour to communicate a range of emotional and physical needs (Carr *et al.*, 1993).

Changes in services

Following almost a century in which large, isolated institutions for people with learning disabilities literally dominated the landscape, services and supports for people with learning disabilities are now more person-centred and individualised (Emerson, 2005). The third sector now provides a range of social care services for people, such as personal support in people's own homes, short breaks and daytime support to access leisure facilities or to access work opportunities. Specialist multi-professional learning disability teams provide additional support to people living in their own or their family home. These services are provided by local NHS Trusts, whilst specialist in-patient services, provided mainly by the NHS, have had to transform themselves from a custodial, long-term care model to one in which the emphasis is on treatment and rehabilitation. Table 4.1 provides some of the reasons for admission to specialist in-patient services.

As the discussion below will illustrate, the authors would argue that this shift in focus within specialist services has contributed to a positive change in restraint practices amongst staff. This is primarily because the emphasis on treatment means that restraint must be considered as part of the longer term treatment plan for each person.

The need for restraint

Before embarking on a discussion of the need to restrain people with learning disabilities, it is worthwhile briefly defining how the term *restraint* will be used here. Three types of restraint can be identified from the literature in learning disabilities: chemical, mechanical and physical. Chemical restraint is a term applied by many to the use of medication, principally tranquillisers, to restrict the actions of people with learning disabilities. There is strong evidence that medication is used more frequently with people with learning disabilities than other groups in society to manage behaviour (Tyrer and Hill, 2000; Linehan *et al.*, 2004). Although there has been a recent decline in the use of some types of medication, such as antipsychotics, it should not be assumed that their use represents poor care. For example, it is possible that difficulties in applying other types of treatment and therapy for people with learning disabilities may account for the high use of sedation with this group (Turkistani, 2000).

Mechanical restraint typically involves the use of straps, specialised clothing or splints to restrict movement. Studies by Emerson (2002) show that mechanical restraint is used relatively infrequently to manage people's behav-

Table 4.1 Possible reasons for admission to specialist health services.

- Deterioration in a person's physical or mental health
- Deterioration in a person's living circumstances e.g. homelessness
- Assessment and treatment
- Planned medication change
- It is unsafe for a person to remain in their home
- There has been a breakdown in the home environment
- A person has been detained under the Mental Health Act
- A person has been placed in the service by the courts
- A person requires a higher level of support because of life events or changes in their condition
- A person needs alcohol or drug detoxification

iour and, where it occurs, it is usually applied in response to episodes of self-injury.

By far the most frequently used form of restraint for people with learning disabilities in the UK is physical restraint (Emerson, 2002). Therefore the remainder of the discussion in this chapter will focus on its use and alternatives. Physical restraint is defined as the use of force, through bodily contact, to restrict the movement of a person. It is assumed that the use of physical restraint is applied as a *'last resort'* (Fish and Culshaw, 2005) in response to aggressive and violent behaviour that threatens to place the person or others in harm's way. Certainly, Emerson's (2002) study showed that the use of restraint was associated with the increasing severity of challenging behaviour. Staff reported they had used physical restraint for violence toward others as well as episodes of self-injury in which there was a significant risk of harm. Studies of parents' responses to challenging behaviour have also shown that they escalated their response as the severity of behaviour increased (Allen *et al.*, 2006). Studies such as this imply that there is a simple relationship between severity of behaviour and a physical response. However, the situation is more complex. For example, Emerson's study (2002) revealed that the use of restraint amongst adults was more common for people with more severe learning disabilities. On the other hand, a diagnosis of autism was associated with a reduced risk of being restrained. Men were at greater risk of being restrained and younger adults were more likely to be restrained. Living in residential care was also associated with higher levels of physical restraint and, interestingly, higher overall staffing levels increased the chance of being restrained.

Naturally, these findings show associations and do not imply causality. However, other researchers have investigated whether cognitive and emotional factors could determine the nature of care staff's response to aggression and violence. It has been hypothesised that the need for restraint is dependent on staff perception and attribution rather than a strictly defined target behaviour or level of threat (Phillips *et al.*, 1996). This could present difficulties in managing incidents, not just because of a lack of consistency in deciding to intervene, but because it introduces the possibility that staff could be motivated by malevolence factors, such as control and revenge. Several studies have sought to investigate this issue. However, as Dagnan and Weston (2006) conclude in their study:

> Although there is some evidence to support the general relationship between attributions, emotions and intention to help ... the link between carer cognitive-emotional factors and observed carer behaviour is not proven.

Whilst studies exploring the need for restraint are inconclusive, they point to significant variability in the use of physical restraint for people with learning disabilities. For those managing services, this adds to the need to develop alternatives and these will be discussed later in this chapter. In the absence of well-researched and well-developed alternatives, it also means that managers should pursue strategies whose aim is to bring about greater consistency in the application of physical restraint that is commensurate with the risks posed by defined behaviours.

The need for a managed response

If the need for restraint cannot be totally eliminated in services then two key aims must be to reduce its use to a minimum and to ensure that it is applied as safely as possible. A major contributory factor to this is to adopt a consistent approach in which the expectations of staff behaviour are clearly communicated. An important adjunct to this is that expectations should also be clarified about the use of restraint for the service user. Research has established that consistency is a critical issue in the success of any therapeutic approach (Emerson, 1995). For people with learning disabilities this is especially important, given their reduced ability to learn new behaviours. Achieving a high level of consistency requires a managed approach to service performance, care processes and staff developments and supports such as training, supervision and appraisal (Turnbull, 1999a), so how can managers respond to this challenge?

The ethical and legal framework that has been discussed and promoted in recent years (Paterson, 2006) promotes consistency with its emphasis on concepts of necessity and proportionality. Necessity asks whether restraint needs to be applied and what alternative course of action could be taken by staff. The concept of proportionality calls for the application of force that is 'no more than necessary to accomplish the object for which it is allowed' (Dimond, 2004). Dimond adds that 'the reaction must be in proportion to the harm which is threatened in both degree and duration'. Paterson (2006) puts forward a framework that matches the level of response to the level of risk perceived, which readers may find useful. However, Paterson rightly poses the question whether restraint should only be applied when there is imminent danger to the person or others or whether it is justified in some circumstances for staff to use restraint where they have good reason to believe that a situation would deteriorate without their intervention. In such circumstances staff would use their knowledge of the person and would normally use a lower level of physical contact to remove a person to a safer place. This is attractive in achieving a more consistent approach because staff actions can be prescribed and incorporated into a person's plan of care. The disadvantage is that staff may act too early. In studies that have sought people's experiences of being restrained, service users have expressed a feeling that if staff had delayed their intervention a little longer they would have been able to regain control over themselves (Fish and Culshaw, 2005; Jones and Stenfert Kroese, 2006). Interestingly, Fish and Culshaw also promote the involvement of service users in specifying circumstances in which restraint would be applied. This could serve a dual function of establishing consistency as well as helping the service user to understand that staff do not apply restraint as a punishment. These are interesting issues and ones which merit further research and discussion. However, they emphasise the need to focus on a third concept within a managed response which is individuality. This means that restraint, like other aspects of care and support, must be tailored to the needs of the individual, based on an individual assessment. This assessment should include an exploration with the person of factors that can avoid an aggressive response as well as what the person believes would help them regain control when aroused.

An individualised approach to the application of restraint is also indicated following studies that have identified some paradoxical effects of restraint as well as factors relating to people with learning disabilities in particular. For example, for some people, restraint can be a reinforcing experience (Emerson, 1995). Some people with autism have also reported that they find restraint a highly aversive experience (Grandin, 1989), believed by Baker (2002) to be the result of an abnormal nervous system reaction. O'Neill and Jones (1997) have also reported feelings of aversion by people with autism when touched. Added to this is the need to take into account some people with learning disabilities who may have altered pain thresholds (Biersdorf, 1997).

Turnbull (1999a), Miller (2003) and Paterson et al. (2005) all highlight factors such as training, good communication between staff and the need to report and record incidents accurately as being critical in promoting a consistent approach to managing aggression and violence. Each factor warrants a chapter in its own right. However, training is an area that has received considerable attention and a growing amount of research. Allen *et al.* (2002) are generally positive towards training in physical interventions, but assert that the main impact of training is to reduce the length of time for which a person remains restrained. Paterson *et al.* (2005) also point to the value of training in reducing risks of injury during episodes of restraint, but remind the field that the lack of uniformity in training is problematic.

The need for a systems-wide approach

In the search to reduce the need for physical restraint, many experts have considered measures that could prevent episodes of aggression and violence. A range of factors have been suggested and explored that aim at *ecological* change. These factors are based on Bronfenbrenner's (1979) theory that human behaviour is shaped by an interaction between a person and the changing properties of their immediate environment. This is essentially a systems approach that explains behaviour such as violence as being a consequence of an imbalance between intrapersonal forces and interpersonal or extrapersonal forces (see Table 4.2).

Ecological approaches have become popular within learning disability services for several reasons. One reason is that, on a macro level, the disadvantage and discrimination often experienced by people with a learning disability is the product of a social system that has low expectations of them and is constructed in a way that prevents them participating as equals in society (Wolfensberger, 1983). On a micro level, ecological approaches have become important in understanding challenging behaviour. Murphy (1994), for example, has explained how challenging behaviour cannot be attributed to single causes such as ill health or a lack of social skills. Likewise, outbreaks of violence cannot be attributed solely to factors such as poor attitudes amongst staff

Table 4.2 Three forces shaping human behaviour (Jukes and Spencer, 2007).

Intrapersonal: Forces that occur in the individual and are often conditioned responses.

Interpersonal: Forces that occur between people such as mother and child or service user and staff.

Extrapersonal: Forces that occur as a result of the wider environment or culture in which the person lives.

or a lack of structure and routine. This is supported by studies such as Sturmey (1999) who demonstrated that the effectiveness of behavioural interventions for people with challenging behaviour is amplified by changes in the social ecology of service environments.

The focus of much interest and activity in the ecology of learning disability services has been the need to develop person centred approaches to care and support. A person-centred approach may be described as a way of working in partnership with a person that places them at the centre of a process of designing and delivering the care and support they need and want. In the context of services for people with challenging behaviour, person-centred approaches offer opportunities to counterbalance the negative feelings experienced by people that give rise to violence and aggression. For example, as Turnbull (1999) described, feelings of powerlessness, vulnerability, of being devalued, of lacking confidence and being misunderstood can increase the risk of frustration and an escalation into aggression. Therefore, the goal in designing systems of support for people should be to personalise and humanise them. This entails personalised assessment and the development and review of plans that are undertaken as far as possible with the person. As far as violence is concerned, this should include a detailed assessment of reasons for the person feeling aggressive towards others and a long-term plan for reducing incidents. This plan must also include a compatible plan for staff that is a personalised account of action that can help the person regain control over their emotions and behaviour. From the little research that has sought service users' views of restraint, it is already clear that they can suggest several alternatives to suit their own circumstances (Fish and Culshaw, 2005; Chaplin *et al.*, 2006).

Although a person-centred approach encompasses many different aspects, interpersonal relationships appear critical to their success, especially between staff and the service user. Relationships can serve a number of purposes, but in the context of reducing aggression they can help a person feel as though they are understood and valued as well as provide insights for the member of staff into how people might be helped to change. In the field of learning disability this process can be helped because many people who come into services are already known to staff. As a long-term condition, the learning disability population is comparatively easy to define, and people with challenging behaviour may have had several contacts with services over the years. Having said this, staff need to take steps to ensure that they make time to be with people and to use communication with and about the person that is affirming and valuing (Gear, 2000).

The implementation of truly person-centred approaches in services faces a number of challenges, not least of which is that much violence takes place in services which the person has not chosen to be in, either because they are detained under the Mental Health Act or there are limited alternatives. In such services there are inevitable limits to choices that people can make, and one person's needs and wishes must always be weighed against their impact on others. In spite of these challenges Turnbull (2007a) points to the need to overcome an assumption that such services are incompatible with person-centredness because there are examples where progress has been made (Riding, 2004).

The evidence for the effectiveness of person-centred approaches in minimising aggression and violence is small but growing. For example, Grey and McClean (2007) used a control group design to investigate the effectiveness of person-focused training on the challenging behaviour of people with learning disabilities. Reductions in the frequency of challenging behaviour were found up to six months following the intervention. Likewise, Snell *et al.* (2005) achieved reductions in problem behaviour using a positive behaviour support programme that involved many aspects of person-centred approaches. McClean *et al.* (2007) also brought about reductions in challenging behaviour using person-focused training. The difficulties in researching the person-centred approach lie in a lack of a clear definition of what constitutes person-centredness as well as the problems of controlling the many variables against the dynamic backdrop of service provision.

Person-centred approaches can reduce feelings of stress amongst service users and thus reduce episodes of violence. It is also important to reduce feelings of stress amongst staff, since working with people with challenging behaviour has been associated with lower levels of job satisfaction and feelings of being unsupported (Jenkins *et al.*, 1997). Person-centred approaches have the potential to reduce stress in staff because they add to role clarity as well as provide a means through which staff can achieve their aims of making a difference to people's lives. There are other measures that can be taken to promote feelings of being supported. These include debriefing following incidents, regular supervision, annual appraisals of performance and access to opportunities to learn and develop. All are important and are known to reduce feelings of stress and to promote good-quality care. However, it is important to recognise that support for staff must go hand in hand with demands for improved performance. Environments that are challenging and stretching are particularly useful in promoting good problem-solving habits amongst staff, which Hill and Dagnan (2002) identified as a key attribute amongst staff who are successful in reducing challenging behaviour.

The need for a broader approach to therapy

The final section in this chapter will explore any reactive strategies to aggression and violence that could be considered to be credible alternatives to restraint. It will also explore a broader range of therapeutic approaches that could reduce the incidence of aggression and violence and thus preclude the need for physical restraint.

There are probably few alternative reactive strategies that can be applied in violent situations that could be said to be truly innovative. Seclusion, tranquillisers and mechanical restraint bring with them their own legal, ethical and professional issues. Many of the concerns that have been raised about the use of these techniques probably arose from their indiscriminate and widespread use in institutional settings. However, if their use were strictly prescribed and confined to services in which they could be closely monitored for their effectiveness and safety, it may be worthwhile investigating them as a credible alternative to restraint. Obviously, for those who believe that the use of these strategies is equally abhorrent to physical restraint, then they do not represent an alternative at all.

Other reactive strategies that could be employed more frequently have arisen from the studies that have begun to explore service users' experiences of being physically restrained. There is a suggestion from the studies that staff may be too quick to act (Fish and Culshaw, 2005; Chaplin *et al.*, 2006). Some service users wanted a place to retreat to in order to calm themselves when aroused. It is fair to say that staff will already use their experience to encourage individuals to do this, but they must always weigh this against the need to safeguard the person and others. As suggested in an earlier section, the key to using this as an alternative is to be consistent in defining the circumstances under which it will be used. Another strategy suggested by service users is simply to take no action. This is probably based on the service users' belief that they posed no threat to anyone. Again, this is something that can only be used if everyone, including the service user, is clear when this approach should be used.

As far as proactive therapeutic approaches are concerned, the field of learning disability has been extremely slow to adapt therapies that are available to the general population. The field has also been slow in recognising that some therapeutic approaches seem particularly relevant to the needs of people with learning disabilities. By far the most frequently used therapeutic approach used in learning disability services is the behavioural approach. Consequently, it has accumulated considerable evidence for its effectiveness across a range of challenging behaviours (McCue, 2000). In recent decades, following concern over the potential controlling aspects of behaviour modification, behavioural approaches have become dominated by the use of non-aversive techniques (Donnellan *et al.*, 1988).

In spite of the success of behavioural approaches, they do no benefit everyone and their effectiveness with some people may only be short-lived (Turnbull, 2007b). Furthermore, as a matter of principle, choice of therapy should be widened as far as possible. For these reasons, there has been growing evidence to demonstrate the value of other therapies, especially cognitive behavioural therapy (Stenfert Kroese *et al.*, 1997). As Turnbull (2000) points out, cognitive behavioural therapy may be seen as being particularly valuing for people with learning disabilities because the technique is based on a belief that the person can gain greater self control and develop greater independence of thought and behaviour. Other 'talking therapies', such as psychodynamic approaches, are increasingly in use with people with learning disabilities. Sinason (1992) and Beail (2003) provide useful summaries of outcome research in this area, but Willner (2005) concluded that evidence is weak for this approach.

Frankish and Terry (2003) reviewed a range of alternative therapeutic approaches for people with learning disabilities, such as music, art and drama therapy. For people with learning disabilities, who may not use speech to communicate, these approaches have the potential to offer alternative ways for them to express their feelings as well as to learn and achieve. However, despite the promise, the authors noted that a lack of training for potential therapists and a lack of evaluation and research mean that these approaches will remain experimental for some time. Further research is needed in this area to assess the potential of alternative therapies to reduce the need for restraint.

Likewise, Dobson *et al.*, (2002) explored the use of therapeutic touch with people with learning disabilities and provided a persuasive argument for its greater use in services. They argued that people with learning disabilities experience significant deprivation in their relationships in that they have relatively few opportunities to experience the full range of physical contact. Most of their experience is of being guided or restrained or, perhaps worst of all, experiencing no physical contact or physical and sexual abuse. Therefore, because some people may become habituated to being restrained, it has little or no effect on their behaviour. Dobson *et al.* proposed that introducing a contrasting sensation through touch could enable the person to discriminate between behaviours that are reinforcing and those that are more aversive. Once again this approach has face validity, but only a planned scheme of research and evaluation could confirm the value of therapeutic touch in reducing aggression and violence.

Conclusion

For those who manage and work in services for adults with learning disabilities, the prospect of working with people without the need to use physical restraint remains remote in the near future. However, this discussion has shown that there is considerable interest in seeking alternatives as well as ways in which risk can be minimised and its use restricted. This interest is sometimes supported by research, but there is no doubt that more extensive evaluation is needed in this area. This discussion has shown that the development of alternatives to restraint, such as improving access to alternative therapies, may not only reduce the need for restraint, but would also promote choice amongst people with learning disabilities. The discussion has also shown that reductions in stress in living environments could also improve working conditions for staff as well as reduce tension and frustration for service users. However, perhaps the most interesting development in research in recent years has been the increase in studies that have explored service users' experiences of being restrained. There are some clear lessons for staff to learn that arise out of these studies and staff and managers need to take them seriously as they seek reductions in the use of restraint in the areas in which they work.

References

Allen, D., Doyle, T. and Kaye, N. (2002) Plenty of gain, but no pain: a systems wide initiative. In: *Ethical Approaches to Physical Interventions. Responding to Challenging Behaviour in People with Intellectual Disabilities* (ed. D. Allen). British Institute of Learning Disabilities, Kidderminster.

Allen, D., Hawkins, S. and Cooper, V. (2006) Parents' use of physical restraint in the management of their children's severe challenging behaviour. *Journal of Applied Research in Intellectual Disabilities*, **19**(4), 356–63.

Baker, P. (2002) Best Interest? Seeking the views of service users. In: *Ethical Approaches to Physical Interventions. Responding to Challenging Behaviour in People with Intellectual Disabilities* (ed. D. Allen). British Institute of Learning Disabilities, Kidderminster.

Beail, N. (2003) What works for people with mental retardation? Critical commentary on cognitive-behavioural and psychodynamic psychotherapy research. *Mental Retardation*, **41**(6), 468–72.

Biersdorf, K. K. (1997) Incidence of significantly altered pain experience among individuals with developmental disabilities. *American Journal on Mental Retardation*, **98**(5), 619–31.

Bronfenbrenner, U. (1979) *The Ecology of Human Development*. Harvard University Press, Cambridge, MA.

Carr, E. G., Levin, L., McConnachie, G. *et al.* (1993) *Communication-based Intervention for Problem Behaviour. A User's Guide for Producing Positive Behaviour Change*. Brookes, Baltimore.

Chaplin, R., McGeorge, M. and Lelliot, P. (2006) Violence on in-patient units for people with learning disability and mental illness: the experience of service users and staff. *Journal of Applied Research in Intellectual Disabilities*, **52**(2), 105–15.

Dagnan, D. and Weston, C. (2006) Physical intervention with people with intellectual disabilities: the influence of cognitive and emotional variables. *Journal of Applied Research in Intellectual Disabilities*, **19**(2), 219–22.

Department of Health (DH) (2001) *Valuing People. A New Strategy for Learning Disability for the 21st Century*. DH, London.

Department of Health (DH) (2007) *Commissioning Specialist Adult Learning Disability Health Services: Best Practice Guide*. DH, London.

Department of Health (DH) (2009). *Valuing People Now: a New Three-Year Strategy for People with Learning Disabilities*. DH, London.

Dimond, B. (2004) *Legal Aspects of Occupational Therapy*, 2nd edn. Blackwell, Oxford.

Dobson, S., Upadhyaya, S., Conyers, I. *et al*. (2002) Touch in the care of people with profound and complex needs. *Journal of Learning Disabilities for Nursing, Health and Social Care*, **6**(4), 351–62.

Donnellan, A. M., La Vigna, G. W. and Negri-Schoultz, N. (1988) *Progress Without Punishment: Effective Approaches for Learners with Behavioural Problems*. Teacher's College Press, New York.

Emerson, E. (1995) *Challenging Behaviour. Analysis and Interventions in People with Learning Difficulties*. Cambridge University Press, Cambridge.

Emerson, E. (2002) The prevalence of use of reactive strategies in community-based services in the UK. In: *Ethical Approaches to Physical Interventions. Responding to Challenging Behaviour in People with Intellectual Disabilities* (ed. D. Allen). British Institute of Learning Disabilities, Kidderminster.

Emerson E. (2005) Models of service delivery. In: *Learning Disability: a Life Cycle Approach to Valuing People* (eds. G. Grant, P. Goward, M. Richardson *et al*.). Open University Press, Maidenhead.

Emerson, E., Hatton, C., Felce, D. *et al*. (2001a) *Learning Disabilities. The Fundamental Facts*. Foundation for Learning Disabilities, London.

Emerson, E., Kiernan, C., Alborz, A. *et al*. (2001b) The prevalence of challenging behaviours: a total population study. *Research in Developmental Disabilities*, **22**(1), 77–93.

Fish, R. and Culshaw, E. (2005) The last resort? Staff and client perspectives on physical intervention. *Journal of Intellectual Disabilities*, **9**(2), 93–107.

Frankish, P. and Terry, S. (2003) Modern therapeutic approaches in learning disability services. *Tizard Learning Disability Review*, **8**(3), 3–10.

Gear, J. (2000) Non-violent (compassionate) communication. In: *Behavioural Distress: Concepts and Strategies* (eds. B. Gates, J. Gear and J. Wray). Baillière-Tindall, London.

Grandin, T. (1989) An autistic person's view of holding therapy. *Journal of the National Autistic Society*, **23**(3), 75–8.

Grey, I. M. and McClean, B. (2007) Service user outcomes of staff training in positive behaviour support using person-focused training: a control group study. *Journal of Applied Research in Intellectual Disabilities*, **20**(1), 6–15.

Healthcare Commission and Commission for Social Care Inspection (2006) *Joint Investigation Into the Provision of Services for People with Learning Disabilities at Cornwall Partnership NHS Trust*. Healthcare Commission, London.

Hill, C. and Dagnan, D. (2002) Helping, attributions, emotions and coping style in response to people with learning disabilities and challenging behaviour. *Journal of Learning Disabilities for Nursing, Health and Social Care*, **6**(4), 363–72.

Jenkins, R., Rose, J. and Lovell, C. (1997) Psychological well-being of staff who work with people who have challenging behaviour. *Journal of Intellectual Disability Research*, **41**(6), 502–11.

Jones, P. and Stenfert Krose, B. (2006) Service users' views of physical restraint procedures in secure settings for people with learning disabilities. *British Journal of Learning Disabilities*, **35**(1), 50–4.

Jukes, M. and Spencer, P. (2007) Neuman's systems model. In: *Person-centred Practices. A Holistic and Integrated Approach* (eds. M. Jukes and J. Aldridge). Quay Books, London.

Linehan, C., Noonan-Walsh, P., van Schrojenstein Lantman-de Valk, H. *et al.* (2004) *Health Indicators for People with Intellectual Disability in the Member States. Final Report.* http://europa.eu.int/comm/health/ph_projects/2002/monitoring/fp_monitoring_2002_frep_05_6_en.pdf (accessed 1 March 2009).

McLaren, J. and Bryson, S. E. (1987) Review of recent epidemiological studies of mental retardation: prevalence, associated disorders and etiology. *American Journal of Mental Retardation*, **92**(3), 243–54.

McClean, B., Dench, C., Grey, I. *et al.* (2007) Person focused training: a model for delivering positive behavioural supports to people with challenging behaviours. *Journal of Intellectual Disabilities Research*, **49**(5), 340–52.

McCue, M. (2000) Behavioural interventions. In: *Behavioural Distress: Concepts and Strategies* (eds. B. Gates, J. Gear and J. Wray). Baillière-Tindall, London.

Miller, G. (2003) *Safer Services.* Paper presented to Therapeutic Management of Aggression and Violence Conference, Royal Scottish National Hospital, Larbert, 4 September.

Murphy, G. (1994) Understanding challenging behaviour. In: *Severe Learning Disabilities and Challenging Behaviours* (eds. E. Emerson, P. McGill and J. Mansell). Chapman & Hall, London.

Office of Population Censuses and Surveys (1989) *The Prevalence of Disability in Great Britain.* Office of Population Censuses and Surveys, London.

O'Neill, M. and Jones, R. S. P. (1997) Sensory-perceptual abnormalities in autism: a case for more research. *Journal of Autism and Developmental Disorders*, **27**(3), 283–93.

Paterson, B. (2006) Developing a perspective on restraint and the least intrusive intervention. *British Journal of Nursing*, **15**(22), 1235–41.

Paterson, B., Leadbetter, D. and Miller, G. (2005) Beyond zero tolerance: a varied approach to workplace violence. *British Journal of Nursing*, **14**(15), 810–15.

Phillips, C. D., Hawes, C., Mor, V. *et al.* (1996) Facility and areas variation affecting the use of physical restraint in nursing homes. *Medical Care*, **34**(11), 1149–62.

Riding, T. (2004) Getting the balance right: the issues of rights and responsibilities in learning disability. In: *Learning Disability Nursing* (ed. J. Turnbull). Blackwell, Oxford.

Sinason, V. (1992) *Mental Handicap and the Human Condition.* Free Association Books, London.

Snell, M., Voorhees, M. and Chen, L. (2005) Team involvement in assessment-based interventions with problem behaviour. *Journal of Positive Behaviour Interventions*, **7**(3), 140–52.

Stenfert Kroese, B., Dagnan, D. and Loumidis, K. (1997) *Cognitive Behaviour Therapy for People with Learning Disabilities.* Routledge, London.

Sturmey, P. (1999) History and contribution of organisational behaviour management to services for people with developmental disabilities. *Journal of Organisational Behaviour Management*, **2**(3), 7–32.

Turkistani, I. Y. A. (2000) Chemotherapy and other physical interventions. In: *Behavioural Distress: Concepts and Strategies* (eds. B. Gates, J. Gear and J. Wray). Baillière-Tindall, London.

Turnbull, J. (1999a) The role of the manager. In: *Aggression and Violence: Approaches to Effective Management* (eds. J. Turnbull and B. Paterson). Macmillan, Basingstoke.

Turnbull, J. (1999b) Violence to staff: who is at risk? In: *Aggression and Violence: Approaches to Effective Management* (eds. J. Turnbull and B. Paterson). Macmillan, Basingstoke.

Turnbull, J. (2000) Cognitive behavioural approaches. In: *Behavioural Distress: Concepts and Strategies* (eds. B. Gates, J. Gear and J. Wray). Baillière-Tindall, London.

Turnbull, J. (2007a) Regional focus: England. In: *Person-centred Practices. A Holistic and Integrated Approach* (eds. M. Jukes and J. Aldridge). Quay Books, London.

Turnbull, J. (2007b) Psychological approaches. In *Learning Disabilities. Towards Inclusion*, 5th edn (ed. B. Gates). Churchill Livingstone, Edinburgh.

Tyrer, S. P. and Hill, S. C. (2000) Psychopharmacological treatments for patients with intellectual disability. *Hong Kong Journal of Psychiatry*, **10**(2), 16–21.

Willner, P. (2005) The effectiveness of psychotherapeutic interventions for people with learning disabilities: a critical overview. *Journal of Intellectual Disability Research*, **49**(1), 73–85.

Wolfensberger, W. (1983) Social role valorisation: a proposed new term for normalisation. *Mental Retardation*, **21**(6), 234–9.

CHAPTER 5

Restraint and mental health

Paul Linsley

Introduction

Despite major progress having been made over the past decade, services continue to experience problems in the area of both violence and restraint amongst people with mental health needs (Foster *et al.*, 2007; Linsley, 2006; Royal College of Psychiatrists (RCP), 2006). Whilst there have been a variety of strategies and recommendations put forward (National Institute for Clinical Excellence (NICE), 2005; National Institute for Mental Health in England (NIMHE), 2004; Counter Fraud & Security Management Service (CFSMS) 2004), the issue of responding to and managing violence remains a concern for both staff and people who use services. Research into the effectiveness of such actions is lacking, and there is confusion as to what constitutes best practice. Some strategies used in managing violence and aggression would seem to contradict each other, and may in themselves prompt aggression if not used properly. A challenge increasingly articulated is not so much the need for new strategies or better clinical techniques, but rather determining what constitutes good practice from what is already known (Health and Safety Executive (HSE), 2006).

The mental health context

Currently, acute psychiatric wards are the main focus of service provision for people experiencing the most disturbed and vulnerable state mental illness. Treatment and support at home, or in less restrictive settings, are promoted by policy drivers towards social inclusion. Guidance suggests that the most seriously ill should be admitted to hospital, resulting in significant changes to the patient profile of people with mental health problems over the last two decades. The natures of service people's problems have become more complex, with the need for urgent and intensive interventions during inpatient stay, and it is within this setting that restraint is more likely to be called upon and used.

Corresponding with a more severely ill inpatient population, the risk of self-harm, suicide, physical attack and sexual abuse on acute and other mental health wards has grown over the last decade. A recent report by the Healthcare Commission (2008) highlighted areas for improvement within acute in-patient care which included the safety of visitors, service users and staff. High levels of violence were reported by nurses, with 45 per cent saying they were physically assaulted in 2007. It was further reported that 84 per cent of those nurses interviewed had been involved in using 'hands-on' restraint and that more than a fifth of violent incidents involved patients resisting restraint or forced treatment. The growing problem of substance use and the high proportion of detained patients further complicate appropriate service responses.

Why are people restrained?

Research suggests that decisions on the use or avoidance of restraints are made in response to the behaviour of clients. Behaviours that typically lead to the decision to apply restraint within mental health settings have been described as disruptive, difficult, asocial, bizarre, deviant or inappropriate (Duxbury and Whittington, 2005; Linsley, 2006). A common denominator of all these labels is that the behaviour has been identified through interaction with others. It always appears problematic in the environment concerned, and has negative effects for the people using services and staff (Hantikainen, 2001). These behaviours are often associated with verbal and physical aggression, self-neglect, sleep refusal, suicide and self-harm, problematic alcohol and drug use, detachment from reality and difficulties in treatment compliance. The experience of 'difficult' clients is often characterised by overt or covert control by staff using restraint, containment and force.

It has been suggested that changes in the organisational structure of mental health and social care services and the introduction of new public management principles have contributed to a distancing between staff and in their care. Institutions that focus on control, organisational rules and directions to staff to 'keep order', with a 'one size fits all' approach, risk triggering aggressive behaviour (National Audit Office, 2003). Organisational rules can provide obvious sources of grievance, such as those limiting access or egress. In these situations staff may be particularly at risk of violence when enforcing rules and regulations. An overly strict unit structure may render staff unable to respond to patients empathically. In turn, patients may perceive the unit as coercive, controlling and threatening, and feel that behavioural options are limited to disruptive, desperate or violent acts. Such settings often provoke the very behaviour they are intended to control. Locked units, inflexible unit structures and non-therapeutic milieus can increase the risk of assaultive behaviour by suggesting that aggressive behaviour is acceptable or even expected.

Segregation, coercion and social control are often attributed to acute inpatient care. Although the definition of mental illness has changed over time, the association between mental illness, dangerousness and deviance is frequently expressed. Mental health nurses remain overtly influenced by the social control functions of society. The high focus upon pharmacology, risk assessment, observation, restriction and restraint corroborate this viewpoint and will be explored further.

Restraint

Restraint has been defined as the deprivation or restriction of liberty, freedom of action, or movement. In broad terms, it means restricting someone's liberty or preventing them from doing something they want to do. In general, restraint is described as an intervention that prevents a person from behaving in 'ways that threaten or cause harm to themselves, others or to property' (Brennen, 1999). Restraint can be executed in many ways, for example, by means of physical force whereby the individual is manually restrained by staff, or through the use of medication which may affect the individual's cognitive and physical abilities.

Supervision of people remains common within many mental health settings, especially when someone is considered to be high risk. Continuous assessment and observation with a readiness to intervene in the event of deterioration in the person's functioning can itself be restrictive and, if not carried out properly, it can exacerbate an already volatile situation. Observation policy and practice varies nationally across mental health settings and differences can be attributed to ward design, the needs of others and staffing shortages. People using services suggest that the experience of observation is neither safe nor supportive, but rather negative and obtrusive (MIND, 2004).

Procedures such as seclusion and sedation should not be seen as part of a philosophy of care. Instead, the approach should only be considered once de-escalation and other strategies have failed to calm. Seclusion and sedation are management strategies, not primary treatment techniques. Conflict resolution, problem solving and de-escalation are the primary response tools for manag-ing challenging situations. When determining which interventions to employ, clinical need, safety and, where possible, advance directives should be taken into account. The intervention selected must be a reasonable and proportionate response to the risk posed by the person with the dictate to do no harm and promote good (NICE, 2005).

This said, the use of control and restraint (C&R) is, and always will be, an emotive issue. Some argue for its complete abolition, while others argue that it is sometimes the only way of ensuring the safety and well-being of people using services and staff. Interventions that address people's clinical needs, and those that seek to reduce the risk of violence by improving quality of life and care, are always preferable. As Allen (2004) observed, reactive interventions such as restraint 'are not constructive, and they are not concerned with chang-ing behaviour in the long term'. No one would deny that understanding and addressing patient distress must be central to the caring relationship; however, there may still be times when it is necessary to impose control on someone's behaviour to prevent or minimise harm. The very act of restraint may have a counter-productive effect by escalating violent and aggressive behaviour instead of calming and de-escalating troublesome situations for the benefit of both patient and staff. Restraint, unless its use is contextualised and subject to rigorous safeguards, may, as Fisher (2003) comments, represent in and of itself a form of violence which 'precludes therapy'. Physical interventions such as restraint should never be considered treatments, but to be ethically defensible they must take place within a therapeutic environment and a therapeutic rela-tionship that safeguards people's best interests. As Paterson (2004) argues:

> ... the use of such interventions can only be justified in a context of primary prevention where there is an overt emphasis on therapeutic change via planned, structured, evidence-based interventions individu-alised to the service user which identify roles and responsibilities for both staff and service user in a tangible partnership.

We see Paterson's sentiment echoed in various policy documents that advocate the importance of working with people in addressing their behaviour through therapeutic exchange and counsel, with some suggesting that those identified to be at risk of disturbed or violent behaviour be given the opportu-nity to have their needs and wishes recorded in the form of an advance direc-tive.

Increasingly we see the use of individual risk management plans with mental health patients, otherwise known as individual reactive strategies (Lin-sley, 2006). These plans provide a link between risk assessment of a client and known or potential interventions. They contain clear statements of anticipated risk and how it can be avoided or its impact minimised. In order for staff members to identify and deal effectively with clients who behave in a violent and aggressive manner, individual risk management plans should be in place that include a gradual progression on measures to prevent violent behaviour escalating. Risk management plans should be made with the input from all levels of care providers as appropriate, as well as from the service user. They call for creative thinking in order to promote what is termed 'positive risk taking' (that is, supporting individual choice and decision making and helping the patient regain control of their situation) and should be articulated in policy and procedure as they relate to the circumstances of the service user.

Physical restraint should only be used by those trained in such techniques and always as a last resort (NICE, 2005). Restraint of potentially violent patients can take place on the floor in prone or supine positions (horizontal restraint) or, less intrusively in standing or sitting positions (vertical restraint) (British Institute for Learning Disabilities (BILD), 2001). The decision to use horizontal restraint may be made unnecessarily if the level of risk in an intervention is overestimated and/or capacity to otherwise control the situation is underestimated by staff.

There are a number of incidences in which care staff are empowered by law to use restraint (Mental Health Act 1983; Mental Health Act 2007). This said, anyone who applies any form of restraint should be prepared and able to justify why they have done it. The action is unlikely to be unlawful provided that it can be shown to be the only way of preventing harm to the individual or others, it is used for a short time only, and it is regularly reviewed with the client and, where appropriate their families and carers, as well as the multidisciplinary team.

Using physical restraint is not without its risks. Aside from the risk of physical harm to the client or staff member, the placement of patients in the prone position can clearly be dangerous (NICE, 2005). It has been suggested that the holding of a patient in the prone position should be avoided or at least imposed for no more than three minutes, as breathing difficulties could result as a consequence of this. Staff are also at risk of injury when trying to place agitated individuals into restraint, and many express ethical discomfort with the practice (Nursing and Midwifery Council (NMC), 2002).

Another issue is the use of pain to bring about compliance. Some approaches to physical restraint (perhaps most notably the approaches to C&R which are taught and used within the prison service and special hospitals) immobilise the arms by employing joint locks which involve wrist flexation (Linsley, 2006). These allow the administration of pain in order to induce compliance in uncooperative patients who are being restrained in this manner. Some commentators are very critical of this, objecting to the idea that staff should inflict pain on those that they care for.

A related criticism is that the notion of applying controlled pain implies an exact titration that is unlikely to be achieved in practice. Indeed, some patients may have conditions (such as learning disabilities and intoxification) in which pain perception and tolerance may be altered, thereby increasing the risk of excessive pain being experienced (where the pain threshold is low) or of injury (where the pain threshold is high). Even where pain compliance is not used, the threat of pain that is implicit in the use of such locking techniques still makes their use ethically objectionable. However, the use of immobilisation techniques which do not lock the joints is becoming more widespread (for example, modified C&R systems), although some degree of discomfort may be inevitable by the very nature of attempting to exert physical control of a resistive person. Staff should be aware of this possibility and therefore should attempt to prevent or reduce discomfort as much as possible.

An additional issue is the possibility that some techniques and practices compromise the dignity of patients, or may mirror and replicate previous traumatic experiences (particularly physical or sexual abuse) (Paterson, 2006). Beside pain compliance, these include taking the patient to the floor and restraining him or her there, holding the trunk, and techniques which push the patient's face to the floor. While alternatives to most of these techniques exist, it might not always be possible to use them. For example, while restraining in a chair or seated on a bed is considered more socially acceptable than restraining on the floor, a bed or appropriate seating might not always be readily available, or if it is, it might be necessary to restrain the patient on the ground before it can be reached. Staff should therefore take the opportunity to discuss any issues the incident has brought up for patients who have been restrained (which may include guilt and relief as well as any retraumatisation) and attempt to resolve them, as well as discussing why restraint was necessary and other means of addressing the causes of the incident (Royal College of Nursing (RCN), 2004). Individuals who have been restrained consistently report that the experience violates personal autonomy and basic human dignity, in addition to the negative impact on physical and mental health. Individuals with other disabilities, medical conditions, or histories of abuse face even more risks, as do children and elderly persons.

Such issues are not unique and arise with the issue of mechanical restraint. Mechanical restraint differs from physical restraint in that some form of device, other than holding, is used to restrain the client (Paterson, 2005). Many devices can be used, from the improvised (e.g. wrist and waist ties made from bandages or sheets) to purpose-built devices including restraint vests and 'ParaBeds' that secure a client's arms, feet and torso, leaving them incapable of movement. The use of mechanical restraints has largely been discredited in the UK and is considered bad practice in all but the most extreme of circumstances where a patient has been judged to be a danger to self and others and where other methods of calming the patient have failed. The argument for the use of mechanical restraint is that it improves the safety of staff and client, brining the situation under control more quickly (O'Hara, 2005). It is also of note that the use of mechanical restraint is widespread across Europe and the USA, where positive benefits have been claimed. While such restraint is not advocated here, it has caused a degree of debate (which is set to rise) amongst health professionals and client interest groups as to how best serve those individuals who use extreme violence as a means of expression.

Seclusion and rapid tranquillisation are other issues of consideration when looking at restraint within mental health. Seclusion is the removal of a patient to a designated room in response to immediate violence or threat of injury, both to self or others. The patient is kept in isolation and the room locked. Seclusion of a patient is rightly covered by legislation, and those providing such care should be trained in its use. The room itself is specially designed for the purpose it serves, which is to provide a safe and secure environment. The use of seclusion has little if any therapeutic value, and should only be used as a last resort for the minimum time required.

Rapid tranquillisation is defined as the procedure for giving various amounts of antipsychotic medication over brief intervals of time to control agitated, threatening and potentially destructive patients (NICE, 2004). This again raises the issue of asphyxiation, particularly when used in tandem with holds that may obstruct the airway, such as in the management of the patient's head. Guidance stipulates that staff who may need to use physical intervention such as restraint or seclusion and those involved in administering rapid tranquillisation must be trained to an appropriate level in life support techniques, including the use of defibrillators (NICE, 2005, 2004). They specify that, during physical restraint, one team member should be responsible for supporting the patient's head and neck, where required. The team member who is responsible for supporting the head and neck should take responsibility for leading the team through the physical intervention process, and for ensuring that the airway and breathing are not compromised and that vital signs are monitored. Again, rapid tranquillisation, like physical restraint and seclusion, should only be used as a last resort when other methods of calming the client have been tried and failed.

Recommendations, staff and organisational response

It is only within recent times that specific guidance, policy and practice indicators for the management of violence and aggression have been developed and publicised. In February 2005 NICE issued guidance on the management of disturbed behaviour in mental health settings and emergency departments, designed to provide a framework for dealing with violent situations before, during and after they occurred, with specific guidance on prevention and de-escalation through to safe interventions, and commentary on physical restraint and rapid tranquillisation.

All mental health services providers should ensure that their services have a full risk management strategy for assessing risk and preventing violence. This should include measures to calm down a potentially violent situation and intervene safely when violence occurs. To ensure that the policy and procedures are effective, and that the risk assessment remains valid, there should be a process of monitoring the risk control measures and reviewing the appropriateness of the policy and procedures. Unless there is senior management support and commitment, demonstrated in policy, which contains individual obligations, it is unlikely that the risk of violence will be taken seriously and controlled effectively. The policy should therefore contain an authority's statement on how the risk will be controlled. It should enable everyone to know their individual responsibilities, demonstrating the importance of involving all levels of the workforce and consulting safety representatives regarding the proposed content, implantation, monitoring and review of policy.

Organisational support and good working practices can go a long way to reducing the incidence of violence and aggression. This includes provision of training and information as well as the reorganisation of work (Mayhew, 2003). There should be a consistency of approach to patient care, taking into account client concerns and requests. Changes to working practice and working hours can ensure that staff are not left alone to deal with situations that exceed both personal and professional resources. For example, there should be sufficient flexibility in staffing to identify and adjust levels to meet security needs during patient escort, emergency responses and mealtimes. There should be adequate cover for all shifts, during weekends, and during shift change. Unpredictable and unremitting workloads may lead to fatigue and a diminished ability for early identification and control of potentially violent situations (Linsley, 2006). Where there is a well-established risk, there should be a trained response team which can provide transport or escort services or respond to emergencies without depleting or leaving another unit's staff at risk. Likewise, managers should be available to assist in emergencies, provide advice, make decisions, and help with difficult individuals and situations. Operational and organisational breakdowns resulting in litigation and court proceedings can be distressing not only for patients and their families, but also for staff. The psychological impact of failure exerts additional pressure upon organisations that are already challenged, given that such events have the potential to demoralise staff and undermine public confidence.

The need to work more closely with service users is also highlighted within guidelines and policy. This requires service users with the potential for violence and aggression to be treated with dignity; their needs assessed; and the opportunity to be, as far as possible, involved in the planning and execution of their own care (Hahn *et al.*, 2006). This recognises the clients' right to make decisions for themselves and take responsibility for their actions and behaviour. Current practice requires greater sensitivity to the social environment and the advocacy needs of patients and their families. Enabling people in care to take risk and make choices while keeping them safe is a difficult balance, however. Central to this debate is the need to evaluate therapeutic interventions in combination with considerations of public and private safety. The ill effects that may occur from a wrong decision may include loss of esteem, anger and alienation while the benefits are the protection of the client and others from harm.

Guidance of differing levels requires care agencies to take steps to ensure that they do not discriminate on grounds of race or gender when making a decision to restrain a client or not (Department of Health (DH), 2003). For example, care trusts should monitor and analyse restraints by ethnicity to assess whether policies that lead to sanctions, including restraint, have a disproportionately adverse impact on clients from particular racial groups. Care organisations will wish to monitor the use of seclusion data for similar reasons. If adverse impact is identified and this cannot be justified, then the policy should be revised.

Prevention is better than cure, however, and a great deal of emphasis is placed on the prediction and recognition of violence within the differing guidance and takes place on two levels. Whilst there are a number of assessment scales and tools to guide the practitioner, the prediction of violent behaviour is not an exact science. What it does involve is gathering information from as many sources and informants as possible, with the focus on identifying factors associated with an increased probability of risk behaviour, such as an individual's personal history – use of drugs, coping skills, etc. In assessing the level of risk, there is the need to take account of both the likelihood and the potential consequences of each violent incident. Enough information is needed to understand the factors which could escalate violent behaviour and make the situation worse. This includes learning from operational experience on previous incidents and adopting an inclusive approach that involves staff and stakeholders. It is therefore essential that staff are encouraged to report identified risks to managers, as well as incidents that have or may have occurred, so that appropriate action can be taken.

Where hazards cannot be eliminated and risks reduced, a safe method of work should be devised. When a system has been developed it then has to be implemented – this can be done verbally or by written instructions – for example, work polices and procedures. The details should be understood by everyone who has to work with it, and must be carried out on each occasion. Staff should be prepared and confident that they will know what to do if a violent incident occurs. Where training and instruction are required then these should be provided. It is likely that you will need a mixture of preventative measures to achieve control and manage the problem effectively. It is important that they are appropriate and adequate for the task and cost-effective. However, prevention is a complex process, and approaches that may be successful in reducing particular forms of aggression and violence may be counter-productive in dealing with different persons in different situations.

Conclusion

How staff respond to violence and aggression has become an important issue in recent years, particularly for those that work within mental health and learning disabilities. The need to respond appropriately to the demands made of those that resort to violence and aggression is highlighted. As with other risks, reducing violence and aggression requires a systematic approach involving a number of strategies. Rapid tranquillisation and physical restraint should be considered for use in patients with disturbed or violent behaviour only when other strategies to calm the individual have failed. Whatever intervention is selected it must be reasonable and proportionate response to the risk posed by the service user. Risk reduction should include prediction and prevention and requires consideration of educational, environmental and other factors linked to the development and the implementation of locally agreed and workplace-specific polices and protocols. As a minimum, employers should provide training and education for their staff in line with national guidelines and good practice, and that this should be commensurate with the degree of risk they face. Whatever measures are put in place to manage violence and aggression they should be fit for purpose, that is it should reflect local needs, both of staff and service users. Measures should also be transparent in there purpose and communicated to all. Staff need to feel confident in what they do in and be clear on what is trying to be achieved every time they physically restrain or engage with a violent individual.

References

Allen, D. (ed.) (2004) *Ethical Approaches to Physical Interventions*. BILD, Kidderminster.

Brennen, S. (1999) Dangerous liaisons. *Nursing Times*, **95**(44), 30–2.

British Institute for Learning Disabilities (BILD) (2001) *BILD Code of Practice for Trainers in the Use of Physical Interventions*. BILD, Kidderminster.

Counter Fraud & Security Management Service (CFSMS) (2004) *Promoting Safer and Therapeutic Services*. CFSMS, London.

Department of Health (DH) (2003) *Inside Outside: Improving Mental Health Services for Black and Minority Ethic Communities in England.* DH, London.

Duxbury, J. and Whittington, R. (2005) Causes and management of patient aggression and violence; staff and patient perspectives. *Journal of Advanced Nursing,* **50**(5), 469–78.

Fisher, J. A. (2003) Curtailing the use of restraint in psychiatric settings. *Journal of Humanistic Psychology,* **43**(2), 69–95.

Foster, C., Bowers, L. and Nijman, H. (2007) Aggressive behaviour on acute psychiatric wards: prevalence, severity and management. *Journal of Advance Nursing,* **58**(2), 140–9.

Glover, R. W. (2005) Reducing the use of seclusion and restraint: a NASMHPD priority. *Psychiatric Services,* **56**(9), 1141–2.

Hahn, S., Needham, I., Abderhalden, C., Duxbury, J. and Halferns, R. (2006) The effect of a training course on mental health nurses' attitudes on the reasons for patient aggression and management. *Journal of Psychiatric and Mental Health Nursing,* **13**(2), 197–204.

Hantikainen, V. (2001) Nursing staff perceptions of the behaviour of older nursing home residents and decision making on restraint use: a qualitative and interpretative study. *Journal of Clinical Nursing,* **10**(2), 246–56.

Healthcare Commission (2008) *The Pathway to Recovery. A Review of NHS Acute-inpatient Mental Health Services.* Healthcare Commission, London.

Health and Safety Executive (HSE) (2006) *Violence and Aggression Management Training for Trainers and Managers. A National Evaluation of the Training Provision in Healthcare Settings.* London, HSE.

Linsley, P. (2006) *Violence and Aggression in the Workplace: A Practical Guide for All Healthcare Staff.* Radcliffe, Oxford.

Mayhew, C. (2003) *Occupational Violence and Prevention Strategies, Master OHS and Environment Guide.* CCH, North Ryde.

Mental Health Act 1983. Her Majesty's Stationery Office, London.

Mental Health Act 2007. Stationery Office, London.

MIND (2004) *Ward Watch: MIND's Campaign to Improve Hospital Conditions for Mental Health Patients.* MIND, London.

Mullen, J. K. (2003) Curbing staff counter-aggression: a key component in reducing restraint and seclusion. *Residential Group Care Quarterly,* **4**(2), 12–14.

National Audit Office (2003) *A Safer Place to Work: Protecting NHS Hospital Staff from Violence and Aggression.* National Audit Office, London.

National Institute for Clinical Excellence (NICE) (2004) *Violence – Rapid Tranquillisation.* NICE, London.

National Institute for Clinical Excellence (NICE) (2005) *Disturbed (Violent) Behaviour: the Short-term Management of Disturbed (Violent) Behaviour in In-patient Psychiatric Settings.* NICE, London.

National Institute for Mental Health in England (NIMHE) (2004) *Developing Positive Practice to Support the Safe and Therapeutic management of Aggression and Violence in Mental Health Policy Implementation Guide.* London, NICE.

Nursing and Midwifery Council (NMC) (2002) *The Recognition, Prevention and Therapeutic Management of Violence in Mental Health Care.* London, NMC.

O'Hara M (2005) Straitjacket may be brought back to NHS. *The Guardian*, 2 February.

Paterson, B. (2005) Thinking the unthinkable: a role for pain compliance and mechanical restraint in the management of violence? *Mental Health Practice*, **8**(7), 18–23.

Royal College of Nursing (RCN) (2004) *Restraint Revisited – Rights, Risk and Responsibility: Guidance for Nursing Staff*. RCN, London.

Royal College of Psychiatrists (RCP) (2006) *The National Audit of Violence: In-patient Care for Adults of Working Age*. RCP, London.

CHAPTER 6

Restraint of older people and people with dementia – issues and dilemmas in practice and policy

Rhidian Hughes

You never really understand a person until you consider things from his point of view

Harper Lee

Introduction

In the UK, as in many other parts of the world, the population is ageing as the number of older people rises. The number of people aged over 65 years grew from 7.4 to 9.7 million between 1971 and 2006, and the largest growth was seen in people aged 85 and over. This number is expected to rise rapidly over the next 20 years (National Statistics, 2008). Many older people are living healthy and full lives, but considerable numbers of them have long-term conditions and this raises challenges for providers and commissioners of services (Audit Commission, 2008). As people become frail in later life, their health and social care needs become increasingly complex and many will have multiple impairments. Older people may therefore use a number of services across health and social care, including day care, domiciliary care, hospitals, care homes and hospices, at different points in their lives. When older people use these services, they require care that puts their needs at the very centre of decision making to ensure that it is personalised and provided with maximum dignity and respect.

In this chapter a focus on older people with complex needs, including dementia, illustrates the challenges for practice, as well as opportunities for improving care in ways that do not unduly restrict freedom. The position adopted emphasises that if high-quality care for older people with the most complex needs, including dementia, can be better addressed, then care for all older people will also be improved. Dementia is a progressive illness that affects people in different ways, usually accompanied by an increasing need for assistance and support with daily living and personal care. People with dementia find it increasingly difficult to comprehend the world around them and may be 'lost' in relation to activities, objects and space. One in 14 people over 65 years has a form of dementia, rising to one in six people aged over 80. It is estimated that 683,597 people have dementia in the UK and these figures are estimated to increase by 38 per cent over the next 15 years and 154 per cent over the next 45 years (King's College London and London School of Economics, 2007).

Elder abuse and restraint

The term 'granny battering' was first used in the 1970s (Baker, 1975; Burton, 1975) and whilst the term is clearly inappropriate by today's standards of description, it shows how there have been long held concerns about the abuse of older people (McCreadie, 1993). Broad definitions of 'abuse' recognise the violation of people's human and civil rights (Department of Health, Home Office, 2004). Elder abuse, in particular has been defined as:

> a single or repeated act or lack of appropriate action occurring within any relationship where there is an expectation of trust which causes harm or distress to an older person (House of Commons Health Committee (HCHC), 2004).

A consensus has emerged on the main categories of abuse which are important to consider, as many of these categories are directly relevant to inappropriate restraint of older people (see Chapter 2):

- Physical abuse – e.g. the misuse of medication, physical restraint, inappropriate sanctions.
- Psychological abuse – e.g. aversive care practices or threat of harm to prevent someone doing what they wish, isolation or seclusion.
- Neglect and acts of omission – e.g. unsafe or outmoded practices that restrict people's freedom in some way.

- Discriminatory abuse – e.g. restraints being applied on the basis of someone's age, sex, race, impairments etc.

(The remaining two categories of abuse not directly relevant to restraint are sexual abuse and financial or material abuse) (Department of Health, Home Office, 2004).

In addition, institutional abuse refers to poor professional practice and the ill treatment of individuals brought about by the organisational culture, management regimes and resources (CSCI, 2007a).

The abuse of older people, and restraint, manifests in different ways. It may comprise single or repeated acts and occur because of deliberate intent, negligence or simple ignorance (Department of Health, Home Office, 2004). It can also occur in any relationship (whether older people are using services or not) including families and informal carers (HCHC, 2004; CSCI, 2007b). In the past, and to some extent still today, the restraint of older people tended to be discussed in ways that reflected an inherent 'vulnerability' of older people because of physical or mental impairments or other characteristics. Accidents, for example, tend to result in relatively minor injuries, yet there is a long held and mistaken view that older people will seriously injure themselves or come to harm, and should therefore be restrained (Evans and Strumpf, 1989). In recent years there has been a growing recognition that people themselves are not vulnerable; rather, it is their circumstances that mean they are more likely to face abuse or restraint than other groups. One way in which this has been expressed has been in the shift in vocabulary away from 'abuse', and instead towards discussion of restraint as a safeguarding issue. A safeguarding approach recognises that older people may require preventive action or responses from agencies to help them to stay safe (Commission for Social Care Inspection (CSCI), 2008a).

Growing policy concerns

In recent years a number of cross-parliamentary reports have examined the restraint of older people. The HCHC (2004) set out to examine the prevalence and causes of various types of elder abuse. The committee acknowledged that the profile of child abuse has been raised in recent years, but the abuse of older people has remained hidden and ignored. In its review, the committee raised concerns about the overt and subtle uses of restraint to manage older people's behaviour. The committee focused on the over-prescription of medications, especially antipsychotic medication used in dementia care. Antipsychotic medication can bring benefits to older people experiencing symptoms such as hallucinations, but the committee found that the drugs were being used inappropriately to deal with challenging, uncooperative or disruptive behaviour, and to create care environments that were characterised by docility and compliance. Furthermore, when these drugs are used with people with dementia they a̶............................risk of stroke and mortality, reduced quality of life

T..t at the dearth of reliable resea...y prevalence studies into elder...the Department of Health (DH...prevalence study on elder abus...omes and hospitals) (see O'F...care regulator to publish a the.....................................[, 2007b).

res...raise concerns about the (J...cation in residential settings D...rty Parliamentary Group on th...ent have also championed o...(e.g. Burstow, 2008; House s...stow (2008) has produced a the latest report, *Keep Ta......* ....er people in care homes. In ....stow's (2008) analysis identifies considerable numbers (approximately 100,000) of older people in care homes routinely being prescribed antipsychotic drugs. These drugs are prescribed off-license and without the necessary review and monitoring arrangement taking place. Burstow calls for much stronger police and criminal justice action to deal with inappropriate prescribing and the use of antipsychotic drugs as a form of restraint.

Restraint in the context of law

'Elder abuse' is a term that has no legal status in the UK - although there have been strong calls for legislation to safeguard older people (Greengross *et al.*, 2009). However, the inappropriate use of restraints can be against criminal and civil law in most care settings. The legal issues that have been outlined for people with learning difficulties are exactly the same for older people, for example:

- false imprisonment – unlawful and intentional or reckless restraint of freedom of movement
- common assault – hostile intent designed to cause apprehension
- assault – act of causing a person to fear for physical safety
- battery – the actual application of force

- malicious wounding or inflicting grievous bodily harm – serious harm may imply discontinuity of whole skin (Lyon and Pimor, 2004).

Recent mental capacity legislation in the UK makes illegal the restriction of someone's liberty of movement, regardless of whether they resist (Adults with Incapacity Act (Scotland) 2000; Mental Capacity Act 2005 (England and Wales)). Mental capacity legislation is particularly important in the care of people living with moderate to advanced stages of dementia. In England and Wales the Mental Capacity Act 2005 sets out a legal definition of restraint:

> The use or threat of force to help do an act which the person resists, or the restriction of the person's liberty of movement, whether or not they resist. Restraint may only be used where it is necessary to protect the person from harm and is proportionate to the risk of harm (Department for Constitutional Affairs, 2007).

Section 1 of the Act sets out five statutory principles – the values that underpin the legal requirements in the Act. The Act is intended to be enabling and supportive of people who lack capacity, not restricting or controlling of their lives. It aims to protect people who lack capacity to make particular decisions and to maximise their ability to make decisions, or to participate in decision-making, as far as they are able to do so:

- A person must be assumed to have capacity unless it is established that they lack capacity.
- A person is not to be treated as unable to make a decision unless all practicable steps to help him to do so have been taken without success.
- A person is not to be treated as unable to make a decision merely because he makes an unwise decision.
- An act done, or decision made, under this Act for or on behalf of a person who lacks capacity must be done, or made, in his best interests.
- Before the act is done, or the decision is made, regard must be had to whether the purpose for which it is needed can be as effectively achieved in a way that is less restrictive of the person's rights and freedom of action (Department for Constitutional Affairs, 2007).

The Mental Capacity Act 2005 sets out how restraint should only occur to prevent harm to the person being restrained, and the amount and type of restraint, including the time it lasts, should be proportionate to the likelihood and seriousness of the harm needing to be prevented. Guidance is clear: restraint should not be used for convenience nor to ensure that someone can do something more easily. The Mental Capacity Act created two new offences of ill-treatment and willful neglect. Restraint is therefore abuse if the correct procedures have not been followed, and should trigger local adults' safeguarding procedures.

Restraint and adult health and social care policies

The principles underpinning the Human Rights Act (1998), including fairness, respect, equality and dignity, are the main driver for ensuring that everyone receives their health and social care services in the right way (see Chapter 2). These basic rights are unaffected when people use services at home, in the community and in residential settings. Health and social care policies for adults, and older people in particular, emphasise the importance of people maintaining independence, control and choice over their lives and their care (DH, 2005; Her Majesty's (HM) Government, 2005; DH, 2006, 2008). The exception of course is when legal provisions limit people's liberties.

The Dignity in Care Campaign, incorporating the Dignity Challenge, aims to promote the necessary changes to care cultures to ensure that older people and their families are treated with respect, dignity and fairness (Care Services Improvement Partnership, 2008). The challenge is for high-quality services to (amongst other things) be characterised by zero tolerance of all forms of abuse, to be personalised and to allow people to complain without fear of retribution. *Putting People First* cements these principles in a joint protocol for central and local government, the social care sector's professional leadership, providers and regulators (Her Majesty's Government Ministerial Concordat, 2007). There is considerable overlap between the social care concordat and the NHS Next Stage Review (DH, 2008). This policy backdrop to the use of restraint is clearly very important, as its use needs to be considered as an affront to dignity and respect when using services.

Evidence on the extent of restraint amongst older people

One of the features of undertaking research with older people is that they are likely to give positive and socially desirable accounts of their care. This may be due to gratitude or anxieties about their care being affected in some way if they offer negative reports about their treatment. It can therefore be difficult to collect information about older people's experiences of restraint, and may lead to some underreporting. Internationally the UK has lagged behind other countries in undertaking prevalence studies on topics about the abuse of older people. Overall, there is a recognised dearth of reliable tools to measure elder abuse (Cooper *et al.*, 2008) and restraint in particular. This has led to criticisms about the amount and quality of available evidence in the UK (HCHC, 2004). A systematic review of elder abuse studies internationally found that one in four older people are at risk of physical abuse, including some form of restraint (Cooper *et al.*, 2008). Internationally, between 3.2 per cent and 27.5 per cent of the general population experienced abuse. This wide range in findings can be attributed to abuse prevalence between countries as well as different cultural understandings. Of the studies reviewed, one in ten professional carers admitted to conducting physical abuse and over 80 per cent of care home staff had witnessed some form of physical abuse. The UK's first prevalence study with a representative sample of people aged 65 and over found four per cent had been subject to physical mistreatment. This study looked at more than just the use of restraint and involved older people in the community (thus excluding care homes and hospitals etc.) but does provide a broad indication of the seriousness of elder abuse and the use of restraints.

Understanding behaviour

> Once you've met one person with dementia ... you've met one person with dementia (quotation attributed to the late Tom Kitwood cited in CSCI, 2008b).

Kitwood (1997) emphasised the need to see individuals' behaviour as forms of communication, largely arising from their needs, rather than as 'dementia' and 'problems' to be managed. Seeking out the perspectives of older people can allow people's needs to be identified and to be better understood. For example, persistent and repetitive walking behaviours (or 'wandering') are common amongst people with dementia and are often a cause for concern, as people may become lost, fail to return or be at risk of injury or accidents. These can be concerns shared by people with dementia, their carers and staff and have led to debates about the use of tagging and tracking technology for people prone to these conditions (Hughes and Louw, 2002). Continual walking may appear aimless, but is often caused by stress, anxiety or confusion. It may compensate for restlessness or boredom, or be the result of physical discomfort or the side effects of medication. Walking is a good form of exercise, may even be a type of communication and is behaviour that needs to be understood, rather than stopped (Marshall and Allan, 2006). Furthermore, walking can be as enjoyable an experience for people with dementia as it can be for people without the illness. It can enable people to remain mobile and is a form of healthy exercise. It is not, therefore, an activity which should be discouraged just because of the concerns of staff. Instead, there is a need to focus on how walking can be safely facilitated, such as nighttime activities for people when they cannot sleep and are most prone to walking.

There will, however, be other behaviours that are more difficult to manage. For example, health and social care staff sometimes face challenging and violent behaviour from people in their care (Denney, 2005; Healthcare Commission, 2008) and older people and people with dementia are no exception (Teri *et al.*, 2002; Berry, 2006; Bourbonnais and Ducharme, 2008). People's mood and behaviour can be affected by the damage to the brain caused by dementia as well as because of the psychosocial aspects of living with the condition, such as restlessness or boredom. Teri reports behavioural disturbance with between 70 and 90 per cent of people with dementia. Berry (2006) surveyed the extent and nature of aggression amongst people with dementia living in 197 care homes. The study found that 137 care homes had recently recorded verbal or physical aggression from people with dementia. Approximately one third of care homes recorded an injury to staff which caused them considerable distress.

Older people may become aggressive when they misunderstand the actions of staff or when their intimate needs (such as being assisted to the toilet) are interpreted as an invasion of privacy. People with dementia themselves have also reinforced the importance of seeing situations, first and foremost, from the perspective of the individual. All encounters can be left open to misinterpretation, and this can become particularly apparent when memory and cognitive abilities are impaired.

> I operate in a different way to you, and need a different type of interaction, which is slower and more meaningful. ... Try to avoid direct questions, which can alarm us or make us feel very uncomfortable. Questions also make us feel pressured for the immediacy we have lost. ... Most importantly, don't push us into something, because we can't think or speak fast enough to let you know whether we agree. Try to give us time to respond – to let you know whether we really want to do it. Being forced into things makes us upset or aggressive, even fearful (Bryden, 2005).

Bryden was a top civil servant diagnosed with dementia. She describes dementia as a dance, where footsteps need to change along the way as the condition progressed. She was a great campaigner and advocate for people with dementia and wrote about her experiences and perspectives of living with the condition. However, her last public presentation describes how exhausted, confused and 'muddle headed' she had become. What had been a 'dance with dementia' had become a 'wrestle', characterised by anguish, despair and anxiety coupled with increased physical impairments (Bryden, 2006).

When people's conditions deteriorate, there is a risk that restraints will be more likely to be used. It may, for example, be more difficult to reason with people, and drugs used to treat anxiety or depression may increase the risk of falls and subsequent injury. To take a plausible scenario further, a fall can raise staff anxiety about people's safety, and restraints may be seen as the best means of preventing people from injuring themselves. Yet restraints can, ironically, increase the risk of adverse events such as confusion, anxiety and falls. Irving's (2002) analysis exposes further complexities and the professional discourses governing the use of restraint. She notes how staff can feel that safety must be the highest priority and for older people to be protected. And if this is not to be the case, then the opposite view, that people should be free to do exactly what they want and to incur the risks that this entails, would therefore prevail. Irving (2002) notes the inherent dangers in these polarised views:

> By putting the notions of safety and of freedom in antithesis to each other, staff could safely avoid the argument that safety and freedom may exist together, both in less extreme forms. The discourse sets up the issues on opposite sides of the fence, and is powerful because of its emotive nature. It dictates that if you do not want the patient to be safe you must want the opposite, which would be the frail older patients falling over and causing untold damage and suffering to themselves. The other aspect of this discourse is that it powerfully and silently packages restraints as humane and caring, despite the obvious contradictions this represents ....

Bedrails: subtle restraint?

There are, arguably, some forms of restraint that are more specific to older people and the debate about the use of bedrails provides one good example of the fine boundaries between the care and undue control of older people. Bedrails are, perhaps, the most widely used form of physical restraint amongst older people.

Older people who fall from bed clearly risk injury. They may fall accidentally because they slip or slide from bed, when they move to reposition themselves, or when agitated, anxious or confused. Bedside rails form a barrier and contain individuals within the bed thereby preventing older people from falling from bed and injuring themselves. However, the use of this equipment may also be used to prevent people from leaving a bed voluntarily. Bedrails may also act as a psychological barrier to discourage people leaving bed – especially when they are agitated or confused. Bedrails have even been described as a form of 'imprisonment' (Dimond, 2004).

Whilst bedside rails tend to be used for safety reasons, they have not been found to reduce the incidence of bed-related falls and injury (Capezuti *et al.*, 2007). They may even contribute greater risk to older people in bed, as people may fall from a greater height as they try to haul themselves over the rails. Rails used on beds that are not designed for the equipment, or rails that do not take into account individuals' size and weight, can cause additional problems (Hignett and Griffiths, 2005). People have become entrapped in the bars, and in some extreme cases this has led to people dying from asphyxiation (Meikle, 2001). Other consequences associated with containing people in bed include reductions in people's mobility, pressure sores and incontinence (Oliver, 2002). More practically, it can also be difficult to interact with people through bedrails, which is particularly problematic when people are nearing the end of their lives (O'Keeffe, 2004).

The National Patient Safety Agency (NPSA, 2007a) undertook a systematic review on bedrails. The review found:

- Few scientific studies on the use of bedrails and the tendency for the existing literature to focus on the use of bedrails to cause harm.
- Bedrails that stop people who want to get out of bed is restraint; however, it is likely to be an ineffective technique as people instinctively attempt to climb over the rails.
- Published rates of bedrail use in UK hospitals ranges from 8 per cent to 35 per cent.
- At least 25 per cent of patient falls in hospitals are falls from bed.
- The risk of fatal entrapment in bedrails in hospitals was less than one in ten million admissions, whereas the risk of falls is one in 200 people receiving care in hospital.

The evidence suggests that a careful balance needs to be struck between the risk of people being injured because of bedrails and being unduly restrained because of the risk from falling out of bed. Staff clearly face dilemmas between balancing safety and freedom in relation to the use of bedrails, which prompted the NPSA to provide education and awareness materials (see Figure 6.1; NPSA, 2008).

Education and training

Education and training programmes directed at health and social care staff have helped them to better manage situations that might lead to restraint. Testad *et al.* (2005) employed educative seminars with regular follow-up support and

Figure 6.1 Bedrails are intended to stop patients falling out of bed accidentally, not to stop them getting out of bed (NPSA, 2008). (Reproduced with permission: NPSA.)

guidance on managing dementia and challenging behaviour as a means of encouraging staff to use alternatives to physical restraints. The education support led to increases in the quality of care for older people and reductions in the use of restraint by over half. One of the secondary outcomes of the study was that staff learnt to relate better to people by taking an individualized approach to care.

Large numbers of older people in hospitals experience delirium (up to 56 per cent according to some studies). Tabet *et al*. (2005) introduced an education package aimed to improve awareness and knowledge of delirium with people aged 70 and above in acute hospitals. The initiative led to lower rates of delirium and better clinical management, mitigating the need for restraints. Fossey *et al*. (2006) trialed the 'focused intervention training and support' (FITS) designed to reduce the use of neuroleptics in care homes. FITS takes a 'whole home' approach, addressing issues such as the environment, working practices and procedures as well as staff attitudes and direct skills training, including person-centred care. The approach reduced neuroleptic use by people living in the home and levels of agitation and aggression did not increase as a consequence of reduced prescribing of the drugs. The FITS resulted in sustained change measured over 12 months.

Resources

Person-centred planning and education and training initiatives to reduce the use of restraint are usually discussed against concerns about funding and resources in health and social care. Critically there are concerns that restraints are being used as a substitute for, or as a consequence of, inadequate staffing levels. A number of studies of staff accounts have shown that people justify restraints because of the pressures on their time and the limited resources within the care setting – this may ultimately constitute institutional abuse. We do not know enough about the causal or other relationships between resources and the use of restraints, yet there should be no excuse for inappropriate restraint. However, we do know that there are pressures on the health and social care system. When services are not procured at a rate that allows for good quality care, including high-quality person-centred care, then the health and social care outcomes for people are likely to be compromised. Improvements in relation to the use of restraints are as much about improving the quality of care in health and social care broadly as they are about undertaking specific good practice initiatives. There are issues about who should fund the education and training interventions that have been shown to change practice for the better. The challenge is for providers and commissioners of services to continue to look for innovative approaches and to negotiate the best use of the finite resources available. More importantly, however, there is a need to recognise that the costs to reduce restraints are not costs solely in and of themselves. The price of education and training needs to be offset against reductions in the amount of neuroleptic prescribing. Similarly, the time invested in person-centred planning approaches will reduce the amount of time that staff spend dealing with anxiety and challenging behaviour. And some changes, such as providing good care ethos or strong leadership, need not necessarily attract a high price tag. Therein lie some important challenges for staff, providers and commissioners to re-balance their financial, staffing and resource priorities in a whole system move towards restraint-free care.

References

All-Party Parliamentary Group on Dementia (APPG) (2008) *Always a Last Resort. Inquiry into the Prescription of Antipsychotic Drugs to People with Dementia Living in Care Homes*. London, Stationery Office.

Audit Commission (2008) *Don't Stop Me Now. Preparing for an Ageing Population*. London, Audit Commission.

Baker, A. A. (1975) Granny battering. *Modern Geriatrics*, **5**(8), 20–4.

Berry, R. (2006) Survey on challenging behaviour in care homes. *Journal of Quality Research in Dementia*, **2**; http://www.alzheimers.org.uk/downloads/Issue_2_May_2006.pdf (accessed 1 March 2009).

Bourbonnais, A. and Ducharme, F. (2008) Screaming in elderly person with dementia. *Dementia*, **7**(2), 205–25.

Bryden, C. (2005) *Dancing with Dementia: My Story of Living Positively with Dementia*. London, Jessica Kingsley.

Bryden, C. (2006) Expressing needs in care partnership. Paper presented to *Alzheimer's Disease International*, Berlin (http://www.christinebryden.com/) (accessed 1 March 2009).

Burston, G. R. (1975) Granny-battering. *British Medical Journal*, **3**(5983), 592.

Burstow, P. (2008) *Keep Taking the Medicine 4. The Scandal of the Inappropriate Medication of Older People in Care*. http//www.paulburstow.org.uk/ (accessed 1 March 2009).

Care Services Improvement Partnership (2008) http://www.dignityincare.org.uk/ (accessed 29 October 2008).

Capezuti, E., Wagner, L. M., Brush, B. L., Boltz, M., Renz, S. and Talerico, K. A.)2007(Consequences of an intervention to reduce restrictive side rail use in nursing homes. *Journal of the American Geriatrics Society*, **55**(3), 341.

Commission for Social Care Inspection (CSCI) (2007a) *Safeguarding Adults Protocol and Guidance*. London, CSCI.

Commission for Social Care Inspection (CSCI) (2007b) *Rights, Risks and Restraints. An Exploration Into the Use of Restraint in the Care of Older People*. London, CSCI.

Commission for Social Care Inspection (CSCI) (2008a) *Raising Voices. Views on Safeguarding Adults. Report on what People Told CSCI Was Necessary to Improve Arrangements for Safeguarding Adults*. London, CSCI.

Commission for Social Care Inspection (2008b) *See Me, Not Just the Dementia. Understanding People's Experiences of Living in a Care Home*. London, CSCI.

Cooper, C., Selwood, A. and Livingston, G. (2008) The prevalence of elder abuse and neglect: a systematic review. *Age and Ageing*, **37**(2), 151–60.

Denney, D. (2005) Hostages to fortune: the impact of violence on health and social care staff. *Social Work and Social Sciences Review*, **12**(1), 22–34.

Department for Constitutional Affairs (2007) *Mental Capacity Act 2005. Code of Practice*. London, Stationery Office.

Department of Health, Home Office (2004) *No Secrets: Guidance on Developing and Implementing Multi-agency Policies and Procedures to Protect Vulnerable Adults from Abuse*. London, Department of Health.

Department of Health (DH) (2005) *Independence, Well-being and Choice: Out Vision for the Future of Social Care for Adults in England*. London, Stationery Office.

Department of Health (DH) (2006) *Our Health, Our Care, Our Say: a New Direction for Community Services*. London, Stationery Office.

Department of Health (DH) (2008) *High Quality Care for All. NHS Next Stage Review Final Report*. London, Stationery Office.

Dimond, B. (2004) *Legal Aspects of Occupational Therapy*, 2nd edn. Oxford, Blackwell.

Evans, L. K. and Strumpf, N. E. (1989) Tying down the elderly. A review of the literature on physical restraint. *Journal of the American Geriatrics Society*, **37**(1), 65–74.

Fossey, J., Ballard, C., Juszczak, E., James, I., Alder, N., Jacoby, R. and Howard, R. (2006) Effect of enhanced psychosocial care on antipsychotic use in nursing home residents with severe dementia: cluster randomized trail. *British Medical Journal*, **332**, 756–67.

Greengross, Baroness and co-signatories (2009) Protect the elderly. *The Times*, 19 January.

Healthcare Commission (2007) *National NHS Staff Survey 2007*. London, Healthcare Commission.

Her Majesty's Government (2005) *Opportunity Age: Meeting the Challenges of Ageing in the 21st Century*. London, Stationery Office.

Her Majesty's (HM) Government Ministerial Concordat)2007(. Putting People First. A Shared Vision and Commitment to the Transformation of Adult Social Care. DH.

Hignett, S. and Griffiths, P. (2005) Do split-side rails present an increased risk to patient safety? *Quality and Safety in Health Care*, **14**(2), 16.

House of Commons Hansard (2008) *Management of Dementia in Care Homes*. 14 May, columns 1402–5.

House of Commons Health Committee (HCHC) (2004) *Elder Abuse. Second Report From Sessions 2003–04*, Vol. 1. Stationery Office, London.

Hughes, J. C. and Louw, S. J. (2002) Electronic tagging of people with dementia who wander. *British Medical Journal*, **325**(7369), 847–8.

Irving, K. (2002) Governing the conduct of conduct: are restraints inevitable? *Journal of Advanced Nursing*, **40**(4), 405–12.

Joint Committee on Human Rights (2007) *The Human Rights of Older People in Healthcare. Eleventh Report from Session from 2006–07*, Vol. 1. Stationery Office, London.

King's College London and London School of Economics (2007) *Dementia UK. A Report Into the Prevalence and Cost of Dementia Prepared by the Personal Social Services Research Unit at the London School of Economics and the Institute of Psychiatry at King's College London, for the Alzheimer's Society*. Alzheimer's Society, London.

Kitwood, T. (1990) *Dementia Reconsidered: the Person Comes First*. Buckingham, Open University Press.

Lyon, C. M. and Pimor, A. (2004) *Physical Interventions and the Law. Legal Issues Arising From the Use of Physical Interventions in Supporting Children, Young People and Adults with Learning Disabilities and Severe Challenging Behaviour*. British Institute of Learning Disabilities, Kidderminster.

Marshall, M. and Allan, K. (2006) *Dementia: Walking not Wandering – Fresh Approaches to Understanding and Practice*. London: Hawker.

McCreadie, C. (1993) From granny battering to elder abuse: a critique of UK writing, 1975–1992. *Journal of Elder Abuse and Neglect*, **5**(2), 7–25.

Meikle, J. (2001) Faulty bed rails blamed for deaths of 15 patients. *Society Guardian*, 31 May.

National Patient Safety Agency (NPSA) (2007a) *Bedrails – Reviewing the Evidence. A Systematic Literature Review*. NPSA.

National Statistics (2008) http://www.statistics.gov.uk/ (accessed 1 March 2009).

O'Keeffe, S. T. (2004) Down with bedrails? *Lancet*, **363**(9406), 44.

O'Keeffe, M., Hills, A., Doyle, M., McCreadie, C., Scholes, S., Constantine, R., Tinker, A., Manthorpe, J., Biggs, S. and Erens, B. (2007) *UK Study of Abuse and Neglect of Older People Prevalence Survey Report. Prepared for Comic Relief and the Department of Health*. London, King's College London/National Centre for Social Research.

Oliver, D. (2002) Bed falls and bedrails – what should we do? *Age and Ageing*, **31**(5), 18.

Tabet, N., Hudson, S., Sweeney, V., Sauer, J., Bryant, C., MacDonald, A. and Howard, R.)2005(An educational intervention can prevent delirium on acute medical wards. *Age and Ageing*, **34**(2), 152–6.

Terri, L. and Logsdon, R. G. (2000) Assessment and management of behavioral disturbances in Alzheimer's disease. *Comprehensive Therapy*, **26**(3), 169–75.

Testad, I., Aasland, A. M. and Aarsland, D. (2005) The effect of staff training on the use of restraint in dementia: a single-blind randomized controlled trial. *International Journal of Geriatric Psychiatry*, **20**)6(, 587–90.

CHAPTER 7

Changing the culture of care

Gail Miller, Brodie Paterson and Kevin McKenna

For the sake of a tuna sandwich?

A colleague recently described a situation witnessed in a mental health acute unit where she was working as a bank nurse. 'Anne' (a pseudonym) arrived with a police escort, Anne had been detained under the Mental Health Act as a result of 'unusual' behaviour in a public place. She was known to services and had previously been verbally and physically aggressive to staff and other patients. She suffered bipolar illness and was known to discontinue her treatment against medical advice. On arrival she was unexpectedly quiet and withdrawn; this was a change from her previous presentation.

Anne was interviewed by the doctor in the company of our colleague and stated she felt unhappy with her current situation and with life in general. She agreed to accept prescribed medication and asked to rest. She remained in her room until the evening meal was ready to be served. On arrival in the dining room Anne requested a tuna sandwich. She was told this was ordered for another lady and that she would be unable to have it. Anne said she did not like anything else on the menu and that she was really hungry, and she proceeded to take the sandwich.

The nurse present asked her to put it back as it was not hers to take. This resulted in a verbal exchange. Our colleague intervened and asked if she could assist. She suggested that it would be helpful if she confirmed if the lady who had ordered the tuna sandwich actually wanted it. Upon checking it was established that she did not as she was expecting visitors who would be bringing pizza for her. Our colleague reported this back hoping that the situation would be resolved. This was not the case. The nurse in charge became annoyed that her decision was challenged and proceeded to remove the sandwich to put it in the fridge.

As she turned to do this Anne shouted at her, telling her that she was being unreasonable. The nurse turned back and advised Anne to go to her room; Anne refused and called her names. The nurse activated her alarm, our colleague attempted to gain control of the situation by speaking with Anne. This was hindered by the noise of the alarm. Three staff attended the scene and Anne panicked and tipped the table over. She was then held by the staff but struggled to release herself. Other service users were evacuated from the dining area as the struggle continued. The staff holding Anne continued to apply restraint; she was shouting 'Let go. You are hurting me'.

Again our colleague tried to assist; she requested that the alarm should be silenced so they could talk. Anne agreed to stop struggling and go to her room. The nurse in charge did not agree and said Anne must receive emergency medication to calm her down. At this point Anne tried to break loose from the staff holding her and they all fell to the floor. Anne was restrained on the dining room floor where she was given medication by injection. Following this she was very distressed and taken to her room in restraint holds.

Anne received bruised ribs during the tumble to the floor. One member of staff received a cut to his head where it bumped a table; he had to attend the Accident and Emergency Department. Another member of staff hurt her knee. Anne was observed one-to-one whilst in her room, but refused to engage with my colleague prior to falling asleep. The following day she remained quiet and withdrawn.

Our colleague was left thinking: all that for the sake of a tuna sandwich.

Introduction

The incident described raises a number of legal, ethical, moral and professional issues. Unfortunately this is not a unique occurrence, nor is it limited to mental health services. This story has been told to many groups of health and social care professionals, most of whom can identify with this experience and recall their own 'tuna sandwich story'. Undoubtedly this scenario, and many like it, will be reported as violence or assault to staff.

The management of aggression and violence has become a key policy and practice workforce priority for health and social services across the UK in recent years. Although historically it has been well documented that violence is a recognised occupational hazard, it is only recently that violence management through violence reduction has received the attention needed (Miller *et al.*, 2007). In the situation described the staff responded to the incident presented to them by using skills aimed at managing perceived aggression with a 'What shall we do when it happens?' response. This approach has suggested an acceptance of the premise that aggression and violence in certain services are an inevitable problem which must be managed (Duxbury, 2002)

The nature and extent of an association between mental health problems and violence is controversial and may be mediated by context. Although epidemiological research strongly suggests such an association, its expression may be indirect. For example, in-patient studies suggest that the immediate antecedents to violence are often conflict between service users and staff (Whittington and Wykes, 1996). Thus violence may result from the indirect consequences in terms of admission to a restricted environment, consequent disempowerment and feelings of being treated unjustly (as in our tuna sandwich case above), rather than the direct consequence of the individuals' symptoms, such as delusional thoughts (Richter and Whittington, 2007).

In care services, emotional issues (such as fear or frustration) may lead service users to react to their situation by expressing anger at the treatment provided – for example, long waits in Accident and Emergency departments. It is therefore generally more helpful to view violence as something that occurs as a result of interactions involving many factors. Gaining an understanding of these factors and how they interact is the best way to prevent violence over the long term. On reflection, the question that should always be asked is why is it happening?

Despite the provisions of health and safety legislation exemplified by the statement of employer responsibilities contained in the 1992 Health and Safety Executive (HSE) guidance reflecting the 1974 Act, action in recognising and responding to violence in services has been rather slow and inconsistent. This is evident in repeated initiatives in many sectors whose observations and proposals often echo the conclusions of previous reports. For example, there is evidence of long-standing recognition of the risks posed by violence to social workers (Bute, 1979; Crane, 1986; Brown *et al.*, 1986). Official recognition of the problem in social policy terms is first evident in the Skelmersdale report (Department of Health and Social Security, 1988). This report was commissioned following the deaths of a number of field social workers and recognised that violence in social care was, in certain circumstances, wholly foreseeable. It stated that:

> Where violent incidents are foreseeable employers have a duty under Section 2 of that Act to identify the nature and extent of the risk and to devise measures which provide a safe workplace and a safe system of work (Department of Health and Social Security, 1988).

A recent Scottish survey of local councils examined violence in social work (Scottish Executive, 2007). The findings raised questions about reporting and monitoring arrangements. Many social workers appeared to 'regard such violence as "part of the job" and did not report "all but the most serious of incidents"". Whilst efforts are made by local councils to collate data 'there is little evidence on which to base effective preventative measures due to an inaccurate picture of the level of the problem'. The reasons for under-reporting are complex but it remains persistent.

All services must aim to move away from traditional methods of addressing workplace violence, which have relied almost solely on reactive measures. Many services do employ methods of de-escalation (strategies to calm the already distressed person down by means of positive communication), but unfortunately many only equip staff with the skills to respond to an actual or potential act of violence by means of physical control, as demonstrated in the opening example.

Why change?

In 1998 David 'Rocky' Bennett died whist being restrained by five staff in a mental health unit. This tragic event led to a public inquiry into the circumstances of his death. The final report addressed a series of issues arising from, or potentially related to, his death (Blofeld, 2004). The inquiry made a series of recommendations, which included a review of medical emergency procedures and proposed the need for a nationally accredited training scheme in the prevention and management of violent behaviour. The report also concluded that institutional racism was a problem in the NHS and that the cultural needs of service users must be addressed. The Department of Health (DH, 2005) later published an action plan addressing the recommendations and promoting racial equality in response to the inquiry findings.

On 20 November 2004 Geoffrey Hodgkins, a 37-year-old mental health patient, died after experiencing breathing difficulties during a period of restraint. The overall quality and suitability of the treatment, care and supervision provided to Geoffrey Hodgkins were found to have inadequacies. The care plans used were templates that took no account of his specific physical health, mental health, social or personal needs. There was a lack of an appropriate multidisciplinary approach to his care and past and present medical concerns were not followed up. Alternative models of dealing with Geoffrey Hodgkins' behaviour were not properly documented or considered, despite nursing staff requests for this (South Central Strategic Health Authority, 2006).

Unfortunately the deaths of these young men are not isolated incidents or indeed occurrences limited to mental health services.

■ Gareth Myatt died at the Rainsbrook Secure Training Centre in April 2004. The 15-year-old was the first child to die while being restrained in custody.

At just 4 ft 10 in and weighing less than seven stone, he was held down by two male officers and a female colleague using the Home Office-approved seated double embrace (SDE) restraint (Ministry of Justice, 2008; Youth Rights UK, 2008).

■ Zoe Fairly, who had learning disabilities, died during restraint. Her injuries were reported to be similar to those of the victims of the Hillsborough disaster (York City Council, 1997).

■ In 2002, Kurt Howard died whist being restrained in an in patient unit in Swansea. The inquest into Kurt Howard's death reported findings in June 2008 and again identified deficits in relation to the care and treatment he received (Inquest, 2008).

Such tragic events are sufficient evidence to confirm that 'controlling' violence in services is not an acceptable solution.

Evidence-based practice and policy direction

When reviewing policy responses to aggression and violence in services 'zero tolerance' is a concept that is often referred to. The origins of the use of the term *zero tolerance* in the context of violence in the NHS are interesting. The phrase does not appear with the launch of the then new strategy to tackle violence in the English NHS announced in 1998. At this time NHS Trusts were charged with ensuring that any incident of violence against staff was reported and properly recorded. They were also tasked with establishing relationships with the police and prosecution services in order to pursue sanctions in cases of violence against staff. By April 1999 trusts were, in addition, required to set targets for reducing 'the growing threat of violence against staff' by 20 per cent by 2001 and by 30 per cent for 2003 (DH, 1999). It was not until October 1999 that such initiatives were officially subsumed under the heading of zero tolerance and to a large extent re-launched as the 'zero tolerance zone campaign'. An accompanying resource pack entitled 'We don't have to take this' was also produced (DH, 1999). Frank Dobson, then secretary of state for health, stressed:

> Staff working in the NHS go to work to care for others. They do not go to work to be victims of violence. Aggression, violence and threatening behaviour do not go with the job and will not be tolerated any longer.

This relabelling of the strategy as zero tolerance was in part, it appears, the result of a campaign by a number of health service unions, particularly the

Royal College of Nursing (RCN), who in March 1999 had passed a motion calling for 'zero tolerance' on violence at their annual congress (BBC, 1999). As the notes accompanying the launch of zero tolerance states, there were however new dimensions in that the campaign intended to raise awareness with the public that violence in the NHS would be not be tolerated. It was also intended to send out a message to staff that violence and intimidation by patients towards them was unacceptable and was being tackled (DH, 1999). NHS Trusts, in seeking to achieve the latter objective, were to be encouraged to 'withhold treatment from violent and abusive patients'.

Zero tolerance was official Department of Health policy from 1999 until its replacement by a much broader program of activities coordinated by an Executive Agency of the NHS Counter Fraud & Security Management Service (CFSMS) in 2003. This followed a report by the National Audit (NAO) office in 2003 which found that while some progress had been made in protecting NHS staff from violence, four-fifths of Trusts had failed to meet the zero tolerance target of a 20 per cent reduction in violent incidents by April 2002. Reported violence against doctors, nurses, ambulance crews and other health staff had risen 13 per cent (NAO, 2003).This may of course have been (at least partially) the result of better awareness of the need for reporting and more widespread use of common definitions of violence.

The CFSMS worked under Secretary of State Directions which introduced a new national reporting system based on legal definitions of physical and non-physical assault (DH, 2003). These definitions aimed to further clarify reporting procedures to ensure a consistent approach. The definition for physical assault, which replaced all previous definitions used in the NHS in England, was:

> The intentional application of force to the person of another, without lawful justification, resulting in physical injury or personal discomfort (Eisener v. Maxwell 1951, Kaye v. Robinson 1991 cited in CFSMS, 2003).

The mandatory reporting process in place stresses that all incidents of physical assault must be reported, whether they were committed intentionally or were linked to the patient's clinical condition. The CFSMS remit includes both policy and operational responsibility for the management of security and safety issues in the NHS in England. The remit is broad, but can be defined as protecting people and property through the creation of a safe and secure environment so that the highest standards of clinical care can be made available for patients. The strategy document *A Professional Approach to Managing Security in the NHS* was launched in December 2003, which outlines the aims and objectives of the CFSMS (CFSMS, 2003).

In 2004, the National Institute for Mental Health in England (NIMHE, 2004) published interim guidance *Developing Positive Practice to Support the Safe and Therapeutic Management of Aggression and Violence in Mental Health Inpatient Settings: Mental Health Policy Implementation Guide*. This was designed to offer guidance to mental health service providers in order that they may review their current policies and procedures relating to education, training and practice in the safe and therapeutic management of aggression and violence. The definitive guidance is due to be published soon. The content of this guidance can, however, be applied to many services where aggression and violence occur.

Similar projects are occurring in other UK countries. In Scotland zero tolerance was adopted and modelled on the English campaign. The Scottish NHS partnership forum published *Managing Health at Work* in 2003 and Guideline 6 covers 'Protecting against aggression and violence at work'. The zero tolerance zone collates information on good practice and resources across the Scottish Health Service (NHS Western Isles, 2008). An interim progress report by the Occupational Health and Safety Strategy Implementation Group, which has led violence prevention in Scotland, committed the Scottish Health Service to a reduction in accidents and incidents by 5 per cent per year from 2001 until 2006. There is, however, no published data to date to assess whether the strategy met its target.

Scottish initiatives also include the introduction of the Emergency Workers Scotland Act 2005. The Act created an offence of assaulting, obstructing or hindering healthcare workers, ambulance workers, police officers and fire fighters. The first draft of legislation did not cover GPs, other doctors, nurses and midwives working in the community, unless they were responding to an emergency. However, since 1 April 2008 nurses, doctors and midwives are covered whenever on duty. There is no evidence as yet to demonstrate whether the legislation will lead to more prosecutions of the perpetrators and concerns have been expressed that the legislation is a symbolic gesture of little practical value given that there are a range of other offences already in existence which could have been used to bring prosecutions.

The extent of the problem of work-related aggression and violence within the health services in the Republic of Ireland largely reflects UK experiences. There is also considerable similarity between Irish organisational initiatives to manage the problem and those taken throughout the UK, both in relation to their successes and limitations. It is unsurprising then that the contemporary disquiet with 'reactive' rather than 'proactive' prevention approaches which has emerged in the UK has simultaneously become a concern within the Irish system.

In response to these concerns the Irish Health Service Executive established a national working group to review the problem and develop an organisational response which would assure all stakeholders that all reasonably practical measures are being taken to mitigate the very serious potential consequences for the organisation, its personnel and those it serves. The working group is a joint management and union initiative which has engaged both professional and regulatory stakeholders. This partnership and linked up working are considered as the crucial ingredients in acknowledging the collective ownership of the problem and the challenge to find and sponsor effective solutions which have a high chance of sustainable success. The group has proposed a strategic response which employs four best-practice approaches from psychosocial, organisational and health disciplines, including:

- a contextual understanding of aggression and violence
- an integrated balanced organisational response
- a public health preventive approach, and
- a partnership ethos of working

Adopting an understanding of aggression and violence within the healthcare context advances the traditional framing of the problem as one of either service user behaviour or staff inability to effectively manage such occurrences, to one which considers occurrences as being a function of a complex interplay between the individual, the service provider, the interaction taking place, and the environment in which the interaction occurs.

The integrated organisational response is modelled on a balanced scorecard approach and acknowledges that effective organisational efforts to manage work-related aggression and violence must achieve a balance between the obligations to provide safe, effective services, comply with health and safety legislation, meet corporate risk management mandates, and adhere to prevailing professional and statutory legislation.

Adopting a public health approach establishes prevention as the core value informing a structured framework of tiered responses. The utilisation of a partnership approach acknowledges that work-related aggression and violence poses a significant problem for the organisation, its personnel, and those it serves. The development of the strategy therefore utilised a national working group which gave expression to the perspectives of multiple stakeholders and ensured that their concerns were adequately and equitably addressed. The group, which included employer and employee representatives, regulatory agencies and professional bodies, agreed from an early stage that the greatest potential for sustainable success could best be achieved in partnership, through which a standardised organisational response could be developed.

The Irish strategy proposes a tripartite organisational structure involving three essential interdependent components, including an executive function in a joint management/union governance group, an operational function in a central project office, and a consultation function through a multi-agency advisory forum. It is a notable example of how the importance of refocusing strategic responses from reactive to proactive approaches has permeated beyond organisations to national strategy (see Figure 7.1).

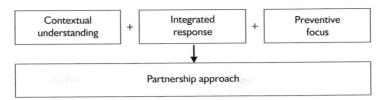

Figure 7.1 Best-practice approaches informing Irish strategy.

In Wales, work to tackle aggression and violence is being directed by the Welsh Assembly Government (WAG, 2004). A number of initiatives are being progressed, aimed at providing safer services. There is an identified ministerial task force progressing four priority areas: incident reporting, support for staff, prosecution and lone worker safety. An all-Wales training passport and information scheme is in place and a publicity campaign to raise awareness is ongoing.

Current evidence

The National Institute for Clinical Excellence (NICE, 2005) guideline 25 *Management of Violent (Disturbed) Behaviour in Adult Psychiatric In-patient Settings* reviewed the salient literature and made recommendations for practice in relation to a number of impacting factors. This document provides recommendations which includes the need to address the environment and alarm systems, antecedents, warning signs and risk assessment, training, working with people from diverse backgrounds, de-escalation techniques, observation, physical interventions, seclusion, rapid tranquillisation, and practices in Accident and Emergency departments. This guidance can also be applied to other services to aid the development of robust violence reduction strategies.

The Royal College of Psychiatrists (RCP, 2005) carried out the first national audit of violence survey between 2003 and 2005. The report indicated that the patients' symptoms were not the primary cause of aggression and violence in services. The report suggests that a reduction in aggression and violence can be achieved if services address the following key areas:

- unsafe physical environments
- inadequate staffing levels
- overcrowding and the client mix
- substance misuse
- boredom
- the quality of training offered to staff

A further survey was carried out during the period October 2006 to March 2007, in which 219 wards for adults with mental health problems in England and Wales collected various types of data relating to the prevention and management of violence. The standards for the audit were drawn largely from the NICE (2005) guideline and the RCP (1998) guideline. Clinical teams were asked to come together to review their management of an incident against a good practice checklist. They were then asked to return an action plan that identified any improvements that they planned to make as a result of carrying out the audit. The most notable finding from this part of the audit programme was the difference in responses between this phase of the audit and the previous 2003–05 phase (McGeorge, 2007).

Previous action plans had listed improvements related to the management of the incident: 'increase numbers of staff undertaking control and restraint training', and 'ensure a male staff is always on duty at night'. However, prevention became increasingly emphasised:

- Increased patient involvement: assessing risk; discussing triggers; creating advance statements.
- Practice changes: debriefings for staff and patients; minimising use of bank/agency staff; flagging up good practice at senior managers meetings; increased access to therapies and activities.
- Improved training: reviewing number of staff trained to undertake observation; use incidents as discussion points in training.
- Culture change: giving clear message that 'violence is not tolerated'; develop ethos that restraint is a 'last resort'.

Training

In 2006 the HSE published *Violence and Aggression Management Training for Trainers and Managers: a National Evaluation of the Training Provision in Healthcare Settings* was published. This comprehensive study further emphasised the need to provide training that is appropriate to staff to ensure positive outcomes within the clinical environment. The report indicated that training in the prevention and management of violence will have improved outcomes if it includes organisational structures which are contextualised to services, a robust theoretical basis, appropriate and salient legal and ethical frameworks, and appropriate standards for trainers; is subject to ongoing evaluation; and include a range of primary preventative measures which are not relying upon teaching physical interventions alone. In 2004 CFSMS implemented mandatory conflict resolution training for staff working in acute and primary care services. This non-physical intervention training aimed to improve interactions and provide staff with the skills required to prevent conflict escalating to aggression and/or violence (CFSMS, 2004).

In October 2005, NHS SMS introduced the first national syllabus for non-physical intervention training in mental health and learning disability services (Paterson and Miller, 2005). This was published with the first figures based on consistent definitions of assault which indicated that staff working in mental health and learning disability services faced a higher risk. At the time of publication it was recognised that viable low-risk alternative strategies to improve service user and staff safety did exist and were already being implemented in some services. The British Institute of Learning Disabilities (BILD) had contributed to significant practice changes aimed at raising awareness, challenging stigma and improving safety, including a voluntary accreditation structure for training providers (Allen, 2000a,b).

Changing cultures

Primary prevention

It is notable that the examples of policy initiatives and supporting evidence described emphasise the need to focus on prevention rather that intervention. A number of potential models to prevent workplace violence exist. The public health model advocated by the World Health Organization (WHO, 2007) represents prevention as having three interlinked dimensions: primary, secondary and tertiary (Figure 7.2). Each dimension is important, but the emphasis is on

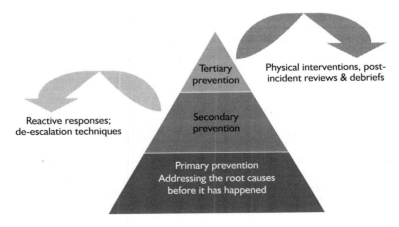

Figure 7.2 The public health model.

primary prevention. A structured approach to training requires primary prevention to be introduced in order to address the underlying triggers.

Primary prevention requires action at every level of the service including:

- the broader organisation
- staff team
- individual staff
- people using services

For primary prevention to be effective, it is essential to understand the cause rather than simply address the symptom.

> Wherever prevention programmes are planned, the context of violence must be understood in order to tailor the intervention to the targeted population (World Health Organization (WHO), 2002).

Many incidents of violence arise from the individual feeling vulnerable, disregarded or ignored. While the causes of violent outbursts are not always easy to ascertain, the effects of the social and physical environment have been identified as potential causes. By considering the situation in conjunction with the intervention, the individual's history and current presentation, staff can start to anticipate the likelihood of violence and construct plans to reduce the risk. Even when a violent act is initiated by someone, the roots of the act cannot be ignored (Bowie, 2006). Paterson *et al* (2008) suggested that these roots may include:

- failures by services to people's needs
- failures by services to meet the wide and specific health needs of people, including people with mental health needs
- the nature of relationships between staff and people using services
- failures by services to meet the needs of staff
- the unrecognised but inevitable emotional impact of previous violence on staff
- the unrecognised but inevitable impact of previous traumatic experiences on people

Such initiatives emphasise better customer care and stress the need for attention to identifying and resolving problems in the care process that may give rise to violence (McKenna and Paterson, 2006). A cultural shift to primary prevention requires training for senior managers and chief executives to be prioritised alongside training for direct care staff.

Secondary prevention

Secondary prevention relies on the need for effective observation, early intervention, engagement and positive communication. This level of prevention relies upon conflict resolution and de-escalation skills. Conflict may occur due to a number of factors; for example, internal triggers, external triggers, and a mixture of both. Staff should be sensitive to the potential of these in order to minimise the risk of situations escalating. Internal triggers can include:

■ Symptoms such as paranoid ideas may impact on the service user's interpretation of events – care plans should reflect the impact of such symptoms.
■ Emotional states (for example fear or frustration) can lead to poor communication and confrontation – staff must make every effort to engage positively with service users and understand when their emotional state has altered (Duxbury and Whittington, 2005).

External triggers can include loss of liberty, excessive noise, poor staff attitudes, being ignored etc. Every effort must be made to establish preventive interventions by carrying out thorough risk assessment based upon a good understanding of a person's history. It often helps to ask people what external triggers have led to violence in the past and discuss strategies to minimise these in the future through collaborative care planning.

Tertiary prevention

This chapter commenced by introducing the many concerns evident in relation to the use of restraint. People enter health services often in acute distress: angry and sometimes acutely fearful of admission based on previous negative experiences (Bonner *et al.*,2002). What they find on admission is not necessarily an environment that offers temporary sanctuary alongside skilled, individualised evidence-based treatment. Instead, as Bloom (1997) observed, their experience may be of 'rigid rules, humiliating procedures, conflicting and often disempowering methods, and inconsistent, confusing and judgmental explanatory systems'.

Despite radical changes in some services, people continue to describe settings in which 'restraint of patients was the main goal at all times' (Horton, 2001). An agenda of control by means of violence which does not acknowledge or explicitly promote self-exploration, accountability and personal growth and development in both staff and service users can implicitly suggest, if only by default, that violence in the form of restraint is somehow redemptive (Bloom,

1997). Any form of restraint constitutes restrictive and intrusive treatment, and services therefore have a duty to seek to minimise its use (Council of Europe (CoE), 2004). Fulfilling this duty requires:

- the routine collection and monitoring of data on physical interventions and other forms of restrictive intervention, such as tranquillisation and seclusion
- the active investigation of the causes of physical restraint at both an individual and an organisational level via procedures such as root cause analysis
- the development and implementation of robust restraint reduction strategies which seek to reduce the frequency, level and duration of all forms of restraint for both individual service users and across the service as a whole

However, national bodies (for example, CFSMS, NIMHE and NICE) as well as case law acknowledge that circumstances can occur where physical restraint may be needed in order to prevent a greater harm from occurring. It is vital, therefore, that where any physical restraint procedures are used, staff are made fully aware of the risks involved. These risks and the associated precautions must be addressed in training syllabi which place them within a legal, ethical and professional context.

The CoE (2004) recommends that staff likely to be involved in restraint should receive training, not just in physical restraint, but also in:

- protecting the dignity, human rights and fundamental freedoms of people with mental health needs
- understanding, prevention and control of violence
- measures to avoid the use of restraint or seclusion
- the limited circumstances in which different methods of restraint or seclusion may be justified, taking into account the benefits and risks entailed and the correct application of such measures

Tertiary prevention also recognises the need for thorough post-incident review procedures in order to ensure that lessons are learned from incidents arising and that action is taken to prevent the risk of reoccurrence. Once the immediate crisis has passed organisations should have in place systems to:

- Review the incident in order that lessons can be learned organisationally and are actioned in order to avert or manage similar situations.
- Review the care of the individual concerned in order that appropriate actions in relation to the individuals care plan are taken to avert future crisis.
- Review the actions of staff involved in such situations in order that any acts or omissions which may have contributed to the incident or detracted from its successful management are identified recorded and addressed. This does not necessarily mean an 'investigation' unless serious misconduct is

alleged or suspected. Such reviews are best conducted within a supportive culture via peer review.

■ Promote positive outcomes for the service user involved. Violence can evoke strong feelings in both victim and perpetrator creating a volatile emotional situation. Immediate management will focus on ensuring safety and preventing re-ignition of violence in a situation, which may remain volatile.

■ Put in place flexible supports.

There is a necessity to provide flexible supports in order that staff and people using services can access at their discretion a range of options that may include occupational health, telephone support, peer debriefs, advocacy services and so on. Staff exposed to aggression and violence can experience a range of emotions which, unless recognised and carefully managed, can have a dysfunctional effect on the individual and the care team (Maier, 1999).

Conclusion

Violence is a problem for all societies. The context, the circumstances in which it occurs, the victim, and the offender vary greatly from one group or setting to another. Services aspire to provide therapeutic care environments aimed at recovery. Unfortunately, it appears that all too easily the cultures of services can be corrupted, leading to situations which are actually predictive of violence, including poor physical environments, inadequate leadership, inappropriate staffing levels and skill mix, poor staff attitudes and lack of individualised person-centred care.

Structural inequalities in terms of power are also significant (Wardhaugh and Wilding, 1993). Organisational policy and practice must focus on primary prevention and the creation of safe and therapeutic environments in order that secondary and tertiary intervention are carried out in a culture of care and recovery not control (Braverman, 1999). The impact of aggression and violence is far reaching and affects wider policy issues, for example:

■ human resource issues: absence management, recruitment and retention
■ joint working initiatives: police, social care, healthcare, education
■ public perception: stigma, organisational reputation

It is therefore imperative that action is taken to promote services that are safe for service users, staff and visitors. The most recent data suggests a small but very welcome improvement in recorded assaults against NHS staff in England (CFSMS, 2007). While this is welcome, there is clearly no room for complacency when 22 per cent of staff in mental health and learning disability settings reported being assaulted at least once in 2006, compared with 11 per cent in acute settings (Healthcare Commission, 2007a, b). Preventing violence in services is desirable in its own right in terms of its potential benefit for the physical and psychological well being of staff and service users. Such prevention, if realised, might also over time contribute to a diminishment in the stigma associated with some service users, a stigma based largely on the association in the public consciousness between mental disorder and violence.

References

Allen, D. (2000a) *Training Carers in Physical Interventions: Towards Evidence Based Practice*. British Institute of Learning Disabilities, Kidderminster.

Allen, D. (ed.) (2000b) *Ethical Approaches to Physical Interventions: Responding to Challenging Behaviour in People with Intellectual Disabilities*. British Institute of Learning Disabilities, Kidderminster.

BBC (1999) Health nurses want 'zero tolerance' on violence. http://news.bbc.co.uk/1/hi/health/292454.stm (accessed 1 March 2009).

Blofeld, J. (2003) *An Independent Inquiry Set up Under HSG (94)27 into the Death of David 'Rocky' Bennett*. Cambridge, Norfolk, Suffolk and Cambridgeshire Strategic Health Authority, Cambridge.

Bloom, S. (1997). *Creating Sanctuary: Toward an Evolution of Sane Societies*. Routledge, New York.

Bowie, V. (2006) Organisational management and culture as key triggers of workplace violence. Paper presented at *Reaching for the Light International Research Symposium*.

Bonner, G., Lowe, T., Rawcliffe, D. and Wellman, N. (2002) Trauma for all: A pilot study of the subjective experiences of physical restraint for mental health in-patients and staff in the UK. *Journal of Psychiatric and Mental Health Nursing*, 9(4), 465–73.

Brown, R., Bute, S. F. and Ford, P. (1986) *Social Workers at Risk: the Prevention and Management of Violence*. Macmillan, Basingstoke.

Braverman, M. (1999) *Preventing Workplace Violence. A Guide for Employers and Practitioners*. Sage, London.

Bute, S. F. (1979) The threat of violence in close encounters with clients. *Social Work Today*, 4.

Council of Europe Committee of Ministers (2004) *Recommendation (2004) 10 of the Committee of Ministers to member states concerning the protection of the human rights and dignity of persons with mental disorder*. https://wcd.coe.int/ViewDoc.jsp?id=775685&Lang=enfile://localhost/ViewDoc.jsp (accessed 1 March 2009).

Counter Fraud & Security Management Service (CFSMS) (2003) *A Professional Approach to Managing Security in the NHS*. CFSMS, London.

Counter Fraud & Security Management Service (CFSMS) (2006) *Violence Against NHS Staff Down and Prosecutions*. CFSMS, London.

Crane, D. (1986) *Violence on Social Workers*. University of East Anglia Social Work Monographs, Norwich.

Department of Health (DH) (1999) *Cross Government Drive to Stop Violence Against Staff Working in the NHS: NHS Zero Tolerance Zone (HSC 199/226)*. DH, London.

Department of Health (DH) (2003) *Secretary of State Directions on Work to Tackle Violence Against Staff or Professionals Who Work in or Provide Services to the NHS*. DH, London.

Department of Health (2004a) *Secretary of State Directions on NHS Security Management Measures*. DH, London.

Department of Health (2004b) *Conflict Resolution Training, Implementing the National Syllabus*. Ref SMS/VAS/01/04 http://www.nhsbsa.nhs.securitymanagement/documents/crt_implementing_syllabus_pdf (accessed 1 March 2009).

Department of Health (2005) *Delivering Race Equality in Mental Health Care*. DH, London.

Department of Health and Social Security (DHSS) (1988) *Violence to Staff: Report of the DHSS Advisory Committee on Violence to Staff (Skelmersdale Report)*. Her Majesty's Stationery Office, London.

Duxbury, J. (2002) An evaluation of staff and service user views of and strategies employed to manage in-patient aggression and violence on one mental health unit: a pluralistic design. *Journal of Psychiatric and Mental Health Nursing*, **9**(3), 325–37.

Duxbury, J. and Whittington, R. (2005) Causes and management of service user aggression and violence: staff and service user perspectives. *Journal of Advanced Nursing*, **50**(5), 469–78.

Healthcare Commission (2007a) *A Mental Health and Learning Disability Trusts: Key Findings From the 2006 Survey of Staff*. Healthcare Commission, London.

Healthcare Commission (2007b) *Acute Trusts: Key Findings From the 2006 Survey of Staff*. Healthcare Commission, London.

Health and Safety Executive (HSE) (2006) *Violence and Aggression Management Training for Trainers and Managers: Research Report RR 440*. HSE, London.

Horton, J. (2001) No protection. *Guardian Society*, 25 July, p. 7.

Inquest (2008) Inquest to open into restraint-related death of psychiatric patient. http://inquest.gn.apc.org/pdf/2008/INQUEST_press_release_kurt_howard_inquest_opening.pdf (accessed 1 March 2009).

Maier, G. J. (1999) Psychological issues in treatment: transference and counter transference. In *Medical Management of the Violent Patient: Clinical Assessment and Therapy* (ed. K. Tardiff). Dekker, New York.

McCue, M. (1993) Helping with behavioural problems. In: *Learning Disabilities. A Handbook of Care* (eds. E. Shanley and T. Starrs). Churchill Livingstone, Edinburgh.

McGeorge, M. (2007) *Briefing Paper Prepared for CFSMS Expert Reference Group Summarising the Initial Findings of the 2005–2007 National Audit of Violence*. Royal College of Psychiatrists, London.

McKenna, K. J. and Paterson, B. (2006) Locating training within a strategic organizational response to aggression and violence. In: *Violence in Psychiatry: Causes Consequences and Control* (eds. D. Richter and R. Whittington). Springhouse, New York.

Miller, G., Paterson, B., Benson, R. and Rogers, P. (2007) Violence reduction in mental health and criminal justice: recent and current developments. *Journal of Mental Health Training, Education and Practice*, **2**(1), 45–58.

Ministry of Justice (2008) *The Governments Response to the Coroners' Recommendations Following the Inquests of Gareth Myatt and Adam Rickwood*. Ministry of Justice, London.

National Audit Office (NAO) (2003) *A Safer Place to Work: Protecting NHS Hospital and Ambulance Staff from Violence and Aggression*. NAO, London.

National Institute for Clinical Excellence (NICE) (2005) *Clinical Practice Guidelines for Violence: The Short-term Management of Disturbed/Violent Behaviour in Psychiatric In-patient and Emergency Departments. Clinical Guideline 25*. NICE, London.

National Institute for Mental Health in England (NIMHE) (2004). *Health Policy Implementation Guide: Developing Positive Practice to Support the Safe and Therapeutic Management of Aggression and Violence in Mental Health In-patient Settings*. DH, London.

NHS Business Services Authority (2007) *Tackling Violence Against Staff, Explanatory Notes for Reporting Procedures Introduced by Secretary of State Directions in November 2003 (Updated March 2007)* Ref SMS/VASV2/03/07/02 http://www.nhsbsa.nhs.uk/securitymanagemeny/documents/tackling_violence_against_staff_2007_pdf (accessed 1 March 2009).

NHS Western Isles (2008) *Zero Tolerance Campaign Resource Pack*. Eliminating intimidation and violence in NHS Scotland. http://www.wihb.scot.nhs.uk/Publications/Violence&Aggression/home.htm (accessed 1 March 2009).

Paterson, B. and Miller, G. (2005) *Promoting Safe and Therapeutic Services.Trainers Handbook*. CFSMS, London.

Paterson, B., Leadbetter, D., Crichton, J. and Miller, G. (2008) Adopting a public health model to reduce violence and restraints in children's residential care facilities. In: *For Our Own Safety: Examining the Safety of High-risk Interventions for Children and Young People* (eds. M. Nunno, L. B. Bullard and D. Day). Child Welfare League of America, Washington, DC.

Richter, D. and Whittington, R. (2007) *Violence in Mental Health Settings. Causes, Consequences and Management*. Springer, New York.

Royal College of Psychiatrists (RCP) (1998) *Management of Imminent Violence*. RCP, London.

Royal College of Psychiatrists (RCP) (2005) *The National Audit of Violence (2003–2005) Final Report*. RCP, London.

Scottish Executive (2007) *Discussion Paper on Recording of Verbal and Physical Assaults on Social Work Staff in Scotland*. Scottish Executive, Edinburgh.

South Central Strategic Health Authority (2006) *Report of the Independent Inquiry into the Treatment and Care of Geoffrey Hodgkins*. South Central Strategic Health Authority, Portsmouth.

Wardhaugh, J. and Wilding, P. (1993) Towards an explanation of the corruption of care. *Critical Social Policy*, **37**(13), 4–31.

Welsh Assembly Government (WAG) (2004) *All Wales NHS Violence and Aggression Training Passport and Information Scheme*. WAG, Cardiff.

Whittington, R. and Wykes, T. (1996) Aversive stimulation by staff and violence by psychiatric service users. *British Journal of Clinical Psychology*, **35**(1), 11–20.

World Health Organization (WHO) (2002) *World Report on Violence and Health*. WHO, Geneva.

York City Council (1997) *Report of the Review Following the Death of Zoe Fairley*. York City Council Social Services Department, York.

Youth Rights UK (2008) *The Death of Gareth Myatt*. http://www.youth-rights-uk.org (accessed 1 March 2009).

CHAPTER 8

Towards restraint-free care

David Leadbetter and Brodie Paterson

Force is all-conquering, but its victories are short-lived

Abraham Lincoln

Introduction

History, as they say, repeats itself. Despite the historical acceptance of restraint as essential to the care and control of the mentally insane, the anti-restraint movement accomplished a dramatic reduction, if not the abolition, of mechanical and physical restraint within psychiatric care (Pitman,1994; Chapter 1 of this volume).

However:

- The United Kingdom (UK) has been condemned by the United Nations (UN) Committee on the Rights of the Child.
- The UK Government criticised by the UK courts.
- The UK Government's position on restraint use in child care has been rejected by the Court of Appeal.
- There have been multiple restraint-related deaths.
- Successive formal reports on restraint misuse and abuse in UK services have been published.
- There are currently two Government committees examining restraint use.

At the heart of the current crisis lies the question of the methods deemed acceptable by society to control the behaviour of users of human services. Such groups commence the debate from a position of disadvantage, given structural inequalities, the marginalised status of those individuals most vulnerable to restraint, and the possibly limited degree of sympathy for their experience in the eyes of the public and tabloid media.

Reflecting the Millfield Charter debate aimed at lobbying the UK Government for the abolition of prone restraints (McDonell, 2007; Leadbetter, 2007; Paterson, 2007) the human service community bring a continuum of perspectives, ranging along the continuum: it's always – sometimes – never – legitimate to use restraint.

However, like refugees from the Tower of Babel, advocates of different perspectives often seem incapable of understanding contrary positions. As one former mental health nurse and hospital patient (Davis, 2004) suggested:

> For me the real issue is not so much about restraint per se, but about restraint carried out by people who think restraining a patient is not a violent act. There may be times when it is a necessary violent act. A person who knows this, and believes violence to be basically wrong, will strive to minimise the violence. A person who thinks restraining a patient is not a violent act will not. They will also not understand why someone would be upset by being restrained and will not be in a position to deal with that upset in a positive way.

Frequency of restraint use

The continuing absence of centralised data ensure that the frequency of restraint use in UK and US services remains conjectural. Its widespread employment on specific high-risk groups can, however, be illustrated by available data.

Adult learning disability

- About 985,000 people in England have a learning disability, and 210,000 have a severe learning disability.
- The number of adults over 60 with a learning disability is predicated to rise by 36 per cent between 2001 and 2021.
- 20 per cent of children and 15 per cent of adults exhibit challenging behaviour.
- 50 per cent of people with intellectual disabilities and challenging behaviour are regularly exposed to restraint (Harris, 1993; Emerson, 2003).

Such figures extrapolate to suggest that the consequent number of restraints = 73,875, disregarding the known probability of multiple and frequent restraint use. Recent inquiries undertaken by the Healthcare Commission into allegations of abuse in NHS learning difficulties inpatient services have amply demonstrated the corrosive use of restraint in dysfunctional services (e.g. Healthcare Commission and Commission for Social Care Inspection, 2006; Healthcare Commission, 2007).

Adult mental health

Duff *et al*. (1996) reported an average restraint rate of eight times per year on an average ward. Wright's national survey (2005) (cited in Stubbs *et al*., 2009) reported a range 0.1–100 with an average intervention rate of 3.13 incidents per month per ward. Stubbs *et al*. also reported a 5.02 average usage in an older in patient ward. A high proportion of mental health service users report being restrained at some point during their admission, with some 40 per cent of respondents to a Mental Health Act Commission survey reporting having been restrained at least once (Mental Health Act Commission, 2005).

Child care

Restraint misuse has reached almost crisis proportion in the USA (see Coalition Against Institutionalized Child Abuse (CAICA)). In the UK it is also a recurring theme in successive inquiry reports, often employed to exercise staff control through intimidation and coercion. Recent press reports suggest that restraint misuse remains a current problem, with, for instance, prosecution, closure or regulatory action against six Scottish child care services over the recent past.

In the context of a total of 29 deaths of children in penal custody since 1990, physical restraint, was used on 3,036 occasions in 2005/6 in English Secure Training Centres (STCs). In a three-month period in 2008, restraint, including severe pain compliance and 'distraction' techniques, was used on over 2,000 occasions across the secure estate, 80 cases requiring medical treatment. (Youth Justice Board (YJB) cited in *The Independent*, 10 January 2008). The Children's Commissioner stated that 'The use of violence and force to control and punish some of the most vulnerable children in society is unacceptable' – a view presumably now legally upheld by the court of Appeal judgment on STCs (case No: CI/2008/0698).

A confidential YJB report published by *The Observer* (9 July 2007) indicated that young people 'report that they frequently experience difficulty in breathing during restraint. There have been numerous reports from trainees indicating that many had experienced difficulty in breathing and other distress during restraints'. The restraint death of Gareth Myatt (aged 15) is perhaps the tip of a very large iceberg of near misses.

Contrary to claims of the 'therapeutic impact' of restraint, its use is reported as generally aversive by service users (e.g. Mohr *et al.*, 1998; Morgan, 2004), and undermines the professional relationship which ultimately forms the basis for control in children's services.

The two recently published post-fatality Government reports on YJB-administered secure children's services paint a complex and somewhat contradictory picture. The NCB report (Hart, 2008) contains comparative data on injury rates across restraint methods, with General Service Association recording the highest injury rate and CALM the lowest. Whilst the recommendations in the Independent Review (Smallridge and Williamson, 2008) for a mandatory restraint training accreditation scheme are to be welcomed, given existing (e.g. BILD) and possible future (e.g. NIMHE) alternative schemes, the potential for confusion through anything but a UK national, multi-sectoral scheme is immense.

The treatment of the legality of pain compliance in the independent review will no doubt be subject to careful scrutiny in the context of existing UK and European legislation and court judgments. Its recommendation for services to develop restraint reduction strategies as a priority reflects official acknowledgement that restraint rates are a critical quality indicator demanding concerted organizational efforts to reduce. However, its understanding of this concept and the tensions between training approaches based within an individualising paradigm, and those which sit within a more holistic organisational approach, have produced inconsistencies. Recommendations for the adoption of the TCI model within the YOI estate, or a similar training system, sit very uneasily with the conclusions of other recent authoritative reports (Social Care Institute for Excellence (SCIE) 2008; see also Hart, 2008) which called for a robust evaluation of this specific model given the absence of positive outcomes within current research. See also European Court of Human Rights (1995).

Unless the required paradigm shift is achieved, the danger is that reductionist, skills-based training programmes will be inconsistent with, and will counteract rather than complement, the collective and group dynamic focus required for effective restraint reduction. Consequently the skills element within training programmes must sit within both a Public Health model perspective (Paterson *et al.*, 2008) which emphasises behavioural prevention, and a Trauma Theory (Bloom, 2006) paradigm which recognises the potentially dysfunctional dynamics created by challenging behaviour at organisational, group and individual levels. Otherwise training will simply continue to emphasise individual skill as the key determinant of safety, implicitly emphasising the culpability of both staff and service users, and ignoring the organisational dynamics which are the real root of much challenging behaviour in group care.

Restraint methodology

The methods of restraint sanctioned by society have little to do with systematic or empirical judgements of safety or welfare, but are largely products of culture and historical use (Paterson and Duxbury, 2007). Restraint takes many forms. Seclusion and chemical restraint aside, whilst mechanical methods such as net beds, straitjackets, manacles, handcuffs and five-point restraints may fill UK practitioners with horror, they are acceptable to many American and European colleagues, who (conversely) may find the pain-based manual methods routinely used in UK health services equally morally and ethically abhorrent.

In the UK, current practices have emerged from a process which replaced the largely *ad hoc* methods, based on individual staff ability and preference, with systematic approaches based on specific models (Leadbetter, 2003, 2008). Many do not attract staff confidence, with Hart (2008) describing the methods of one widely used system (TCI) as 'universally disliked'. The predominantly pain-based 'control and restraint' (C&R) system employed by many UK services remains the focus of specific criticism.

In endorsing Article 3 of the Human Rights Act 1998 and the UN Committee on the Rights of the Child's statement that 'deliberate infliction of pain is not permitted as a form of control of juveniles', the court of Appeal Judgment (case No: CI/2008/0698) in the context of the deaths of Gareth Myatt and Adam Rickwood may raise interesting implications for the use of pain-based approaches with other populations. In stressing youth and vulnerability in their judgment it is reasonable to assume that (general rights under a duty of care aside), such methods are to be deemed equally unacceptable when used with other vulnerable groups such as older people, mental health patients and learning disabled adults, who are known to run the greatest risk of restraint by such methods, especially in UK health services. As Baker and Allan (2001) suggest, beyond such specific arguments, pain-based methods are to be presumed to be potentially illegal where alternative non-pain based methods are potentially effective – a position which available data increasingly support. Whether the Government will challenge this judgment in the House of Lords will provide an interesting demonstration of the priority of public service user welfare over political self-interest.

In the context of the current market economy there may be up to 700 restraint-training providers in the UK (Tucker, 2004), including commercial companies, universities, putative 'institutes' and public sector bodies. Most describing their 'products' and methods as 'safe, non-violent, proven, therapeutic', etc. In the continuing absence of regulation, valid research (Sailas and Fenton, 2000), national reporting mechanisms, training provider audit data etc., these claims remain unproven. Such statements have their roots in marketing rather than empiricism. Many widely employed training models continue to promote restraint methods which are associated with restraint fatalities and are specifically advised against in official guidance. Many systems have high, yet largely unperceived, levels of injury, both in training (up to 29 per cent; Lee *et al.*, 2001) and operational use (up to 25 per cent; Carlile, 2006) and result in extreme trauma for service users and staff alike (Sequeira and Hallstead, 2001, 2004; Stubbs *et al.*, 2009).

Confounding factors

Social inclusion and community care policies have, of necessity, expanded restraint use beyond the psychiatric services into the general health, social care and education communities, leading to 'Concerns about the plethora of methods of PI [physical intervention] and the lack of information and research into their efficacy' (Murphy *et al.*, 2003) and the diverse and excessive range of skills taught with no proof of relevance or effectiveness (Bleetman and Boatman, 2001).

The ability of the average human service worker to safely implement complex restraint techniques is increasingly questioned. Although some attention has been given to the issue of skill acquisition (Bell and Stark, 1998) and retention (Holdon and Curry, 2008), such training provider defences implicitly assume the safety of the taught methodology and that injuries and fatalities are the result of staff incompetence, or 'performance drift', i.e. unauthorised adaptations, rather than the inherent dangers of the approved restraint methods themselves – a perception sitting within an established, if ignoble, 'victim blaming' tradition. Hence improved skill retention and enhanced competence in dangerous restraint procedures merely ensures that occasional risk is replaced with consistently unsafe practice. As Morrison (2002) concludes in a review of 12 restraint-related deaths 'staff followed the book to the letter. It is just that the book is wrong'.

Many commentators have expressed concern regarding this *laissez faire* social policy context and the difficulties of progressing a free, objective debate on restraint safety, often hampered by the 'cult like' (Allan, 1998) activities of some training providers and the employment of highly questionable promotional methods.

Whilst commentators have historically attempted to draw attention to this potential time bomb (e.g. Leadbetter, 1994; Leadbetter and Paterson, 1996) a criterion-based debate on restraint safety is only slowly emerging. Increased recognition has been given to the problem of 'fragility' (Paterson *et al.*, 2008):

A technique is deemed fragile if small adjustments (movement or pressure) to the procedure (either intentionally or unintentionally) are likely to result in intentional, or unintentional injury or severe pain to an individual.

In attempting to draw conclusions from the emergent restraint safety literature, Paterson and Duxbury (2007) list the most commonly employed 'fragile' methods as:

- choke and strangle holds
- prone restraint (face down)
- supine restraint (face up)
- hyperflexion (bending over from the waist)
- basket holds (hands held across the body from the front)
- joints held in 'close packed' positions (i.e. locked)
- pain compliance

'Violence and aggression' (V&A) training has become a principal organisational response to challenging behaviour. Some programmes do appear to increase safety (Allen, 2000a; Perkins and Leadbetter, 2002; Crisis, Aggression, Limitation and Management (CALM) Training, 2001–2007). However, populist assumptions about its general benefits are increasingly questioned. Many widely employed models remain unsupported by valid outcome data. Some evaluative studies also point to negative outcomes, including increased incidents, injuries and restraints (Titus, 1989; Baker and Bissimere, 2000; Waclawski, 2004; Bowers *et al.*, 2006). Contrary to popular belief, violence and aggression training is not effect neutral. It may equally act to deskill and disempower staff (Zarola and Leather, 2006; Allen, 2000a; McDonnel, 2007; Royal College of Psychiatrists (RCP),1998, 2005). As discussed in the Health and Safety Executive (HSE) report (Zarola and Leather, 2006) such training may 'individualise' (Johnstone, 1988) the problem of occupational aggression, promoting a 'reductionist' perspective, where the problem is framed (Paterson *et al.*, 2008) primarily as one of security. This approach presents client pathology as the primary causal agent and staff skill, achieved through training, as the main remedy – an approach which potentially promotes and maintains organisational 'blame cultures', obscuring the organisational roots of much violent service user behaviour and maintains a 'false paradigm'. Ultimately staff can be highly skilled, yet may still face assault in 'toxic organisations' (Bowie, 2006) whose primary ethos is corrupt and which fail to address the needs of service users whose challenging behaviour may itself be the manifestation of social crisis and personal trauma.

An invisible epidemic made visible

In the USA the restraint death toll may be as high as 150 deaths per year (General Accounting Office, 1999). Whilst similar UK estimates are notable by their absence, the seminal study (Paterson *et al.*, 2003) estimated a restraint death toll of 12 based on media coverage, to which subsequent fatalities bring the probable total to more than 21.

USA

In both the USA and UK the media have played a vital role in exposing the national scandal of restraint misuse. In the USA the Connecticut newspaper *The Hartford Courant* published a database (Weiss *et al.*, 1998) of 142 restraint deaths in human services. The consequent national debate prompted a number of responses including the National Association of State Mental Health Program Directors (NASMHPD) initiative (Hucksthorn, 2005) based on the six core strategies document for restraint reduction in US mental health services.

In child care, Congress's response included an $8 million grant administered by the Child Welfare League of America (CWLA) for a three-year, five-site study on restraint and seclusion in child care, pre- and post-training. A team led by the first author achieved the lowest injury figures (CWLA, 2004: site E). The ensuing debate has included exemplary publications (e.g. Nunno *et al.*, 2008; Colton, 2004), which have focused primarily on organisational strategies for restraint reduction, rather than the UK focus on technique safety. As one significant UK report suggests, 'The apparent lack of interest and leadership in reducing the use of restrictive approaches to challenging behaviour is surprising' (Deveau and McGill, 2007).

UK

The exposure of restraint abuse in a Kent Care home by Donal McIntyre of the BBC (BBC, 1999) provided the catalyst for the UK restraint debate. It exposed the scandal of restraint abuse, the lack of Government guidance, and the unregulated market economy of restraint training. Two significant developments then ensued. Firstly, the Physical Interventions Training Accreditation scheme was set up, administered by the British Institute for Learning Disability (BILD), and secondly the *Joint Guidance for Learning Disabled Children and Adults* (Department of Health/Department for Education and Skills, 2002) was published.

Whilst the BILD scheme led the way, ultimately progress has foundered on the rock of government underfunding, voluntarism and the unwillingness to regulate, police or fund existing measures and controls. Progress often requires the catalyst of tragedy, which the restraint deaths of Gareth Myatt and Adam Rickwood in secure services in England may sadly provide.

Whilst the BILD accreditation scheme remains an exemplary initiative, undertaken against significant obstacles, it has, to date, not addressed the safety and liability implications of the restraint methods taught by accredited organisations. However, consequent to funding from the UK YJB for England and Wales, BILD has coordinated the development of a validated restraint safety evaluation instrument which could potentially be used as the basis for regulatory action (Martin *et al.*, 2008). We now have the means to assess technique safety. Time will tell if the political will exists. Effective regulation of restraint and violence management training is certainly long overdue.

An unholy combination

Human services are facing increased demands to support individuals with 'challenging behaviour'. However, they operate within a social context which significantly impedes their ability to do so. As the exemplary RCP *et al.* (2008) report suggests, given the impact of staff and organisational behaviour on the development of challenging behaviour, it is essential to staff services with 'reflective practitioners', who are able to look beyond the presenting behaviour to the underlying functions and needs which such behaviours express. Organisations and individuals must also eschew dominant 'blame responses' and create a 'learning organisation' (Argyris and Schön, 1978; Birleson, 1999) which accepts that mistakes will be made, but which does not accept the failure to learn from them. However, services face multiple impediments.

Structural impediments

- **Status**: low status and poor conditions of the care/health/education sector workforce (e.g. auxiliary staff, rather than professionals are most exposed to risk behaviours).
- **Recruitment**: recruitment problems. Reliance on temporary/agency staff, high sickness levels lead to poor relationships and interaction levels.
- **Training**: poor levels of training. Emphasis on competency-based training (e.g. National/Scottish Vocational Qualifications).
- **Task performance**: emphasis on task performance rather than behavioural analysis, reflection or interaction with service users.
- **Lack of individualised planning**: few challenging service users have detailed care plans (RCP (2005) suggests < 2 per cent). Staff often cannot, or do not, follow them.

- **Multidisciplinary working**: difficulties in accessing specialist support. Competing professional perspectives. Status differentials.
- **Restrictive unit cultures**: service beliefs which emphasise internal causality of behaviour and resulting emphasis on restrictive and punitive responses leading to an emphasis on demand based (*'do this – don't do that'*) staff/service user interactions. Absence of a clear organisational direction/philosophy or theoretical practice. Framework leading to client 'warehousing'.

As Bloom (1997) observes the service user experience may therefore be of 'rigid rules, humiliating procedures, conflicting and often disempowering methods, and inconsistent, confusing and judgmental explanatory systems'.

- **Policy structures**: absence and/or inadequacy of policy structures. Policies are not known to staff, or followed.
- **Leadership**: poor leadership. Lack of vision or goals. Failure to support staff. Emphasis on managerialism.

In discussing lack of placement competence the RCP (2005) report concludes:

> Staff teams should not be looking for quick fix solutions to what may be lifelong patterns of behaviour. They need to be trained, supported and managed in such a way that they can promote positive interactions that may bring about increased participation, independence, choice, and inclusion within local communities. ... The requirement for staff to work in skilled, well organised ways is diminished by the belief that the problem lies in the person and that they can be cured, usually somewhere else.

Paterson *et al.* (2008) suggest that these factors crystallise in the issue of staff disempowerment. Staff may be fearful of service user behaviour and under pressure by managers to exercise control, and blamed when they fail to do so. Staff therefore attempt to exercise control by coercive interactions and use of authority, leading to increased power struggles. Quick-fix responses, such as ineffective 'zero tolerance' approaches (see Paterson *et al.*, 2008) or off-the-shelf crisis management training, further define the problem as a 'staff skill deficit' and sustain and encourage dysfunctional reductionist approaches and service cultures. At worst, staff exposed to violence can attempt to exorcise their own fear and anger by seeking to inspire fear in the patient population. The belief that 'fear (*is*) the most effectual principle to reduce the insane to orderly conduct' repulsed Tuke (1882), but to assume that such long established discourses no longer exert any influence on practice is naive. In the context of the current regulatory vacuum, as Baker and Allen (2001) suggest:

Unsafe Staff + unsafe services + unsafe service users + unsafe restraint methods = Potential Abuse.

The RCP report (2005) lists the national consequences as:

- service deficiencies
- inability to undertake required care plans
- poor levels of knowledge and skills
- use of aversive or punitive measures of control
- deficit of staff expertise and lack of training
- high staff turnover
- emphasis on reactive crisis management methods rather than proper preventive and ecological strategies
- staff inability to cope with challenging behaviour
- exclusion from services
- increased costs
- management failure

Leading from the front

Concerned managers may be tempted to simply mandate reduced restraint use. Whilst this can be effective (e.g. Davidson *et al.*, 1984 cited in CWLA, 2004), in many services the factors shaping high restraint use may be complex and endemic.

Fundamental to any change process is the recognition of the bankruptcy of the prevailing security paradigm: the emphasis on service user pathology and individual skill. Its legacy in terms of the disempowerment of both staff and service users and the increased psychological and fiscal costs of placement breakdown are now clearly delineated in the literature.

Occupational violence in human services is an organic, interactive phenomenon. The organisation can be visualised as a sentient system with beliefs, learned behaviours, skill sets and defence mechanisms, which will act against individuals with perverse ideas about service user rights or restraint reduction. As an overarching philosophy reliance on crisis management (i.e. secondary prevention) must be replaced by a public health model approach (Sethi *et al.*, 2004; Paterson *et al.*, 2008; Braverman, 1999) in which primary prevention, the identification and reduction of the organisational factors which act to encourage and trigger challenging behaviour, assume the priority. Data and systematic analytic approaches such as functional analysis (O'Neill *et al.*, 1997) and root cause analysis (Joint Commission on Accreditation of Healthcare, 2005) play a potentially crucial role.

Tertiary prevention is a further priority. Action to support both staff and service users involved in confrontations to reduce trauma, restore relationships, gain behavioural insight, and to enable the learning organisation to glean the required insights regarding the adequacy of current practices. As the chairperson of the UN Committee on the Rights of the Child suggests:

> It is my opinion that the adoption of a public health model to reduce violence and restraints in children's residential care facilities, as suggested by Paterson, Leadbetter, Miller and Crighton (2008), can best be realised by a full respect for and implementation of the rights of the child s enshrined in the Convention of the Rights of the Child (Jaap Doek cited in Nunno, 2008).

Aggression management is unlike other areas of practice, in that its aversive impact strikes to the core of a range of primitive human responses. It is not necessarily amenable to knowledge- or information-based approaches alone. Staff and managers often know what they should do – but don't do it.

Individual psychological anger management interventions draw heavily on cognitive behavioural models (e.g. Novaco, 1975; Meischenbaum, 1977). Applied to organisations we can recognise the reciprocal influence of action (restraint reduction); cognition (individual values and service culture) and emotion (fear, anger, ego, needs). All three must be addressed to achieve organisational change (as illustrated in Figure 8.1).

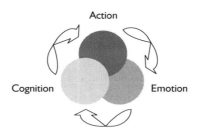

Figure 8.1 Agency action – the three interlinked imperatives.

Action on these three modalities can be discerned in the extensive case study literature which is almost exclusively from the USA. Whilst many individual organisations have achieved significant results, the common conclusions reached in the three most prominent initiatives serve as a template for restraint reduction:

1. NASMHPD (1999) called on services to:

   Conduct root-cause analysis to understand their entire system of care, including interactions between individuals and staff that precipitate seclusion and restraint events.

   Factors suggested for examination included (a) individual and staff demographic factors that influence program culture; (b) staff qualifications, length of employment, and salaries; (c) training available to staff; and (d) differences between shifts.
2. The CWLA (2004) restraint and seclusion reduction project in child care identified a similar list of conclusions.
3. Colton (2004) reviewed 80 publications on restraint reduction, identifying common themes. The resulting exemplary audit tool can be used to assess organisational readiness for restraint reduction initiative (See Table 8.1).

Table 8.1 Summary of components of restraint reduction strategies.

CWLA	NASMHPD	Colton
Strong leadership	Leadership	Leadership
Tracking restraints through data	Use of data	Systems evaluation and quality improvement
Regular training	Workforce development	Orientation and training of caregiver staff
A person-centred organisational culture	Risk assessment	Programmatic structure
Relationship-based treatment milieu	Consumer involvement	Environmental factors
	De-briefing	Processing after the event
		Timely and responsive treatment planning
		Communication and consumer involvement
		Staffing

The restraint reduction jigsaw

In many ways it has required tragedy and an immense research effort to confirm what we already know. There is no quick fix! These conclusions suggest that, although sometimes necessary, restraint use is predominantly a failure of simple good practice. Emergent research demonstrates the bankruptcy of the traditional Neo-Conservative perspective. Challenging behaviour, although complex, is heavily influenced by the quality of the service and its responsiveness to individual need. Reflecting this Co-Creationist model (Paterson and Miller, 2006), Horner (in RCP, 2005) suggests 'Our job is not to fix people, but to design effective environments'. Although no one approach can fit all situations, the conclusions from the current debate generally endorse the technology of positive behavioural support (Koegel *et al.*, 1996), a perspective which emphasises:

> the importance of teaching more acceptable forms of behaviour, as an alternative to aggression identifying and reducing the aversiveness of habitual trigger situations (see Emerson and Hatton, 2000; RCP, 2005)

This general perspective may lend saliency to the specific synthesising themes in the literature on successful restraint reduction, discussed below.

A person-centred culture

> The link between institutionalisation and aggression is well known. Where service users perceive that they do not have an emotional stake in the service, challenges result. Where staff feel disempowered, conformance with agency rules and procedures, enforced by coercion becomes a hallmark of corrupted cultures of care (Wardhaugh and Wilding, 1993).

Consistency of staff attitude and response is a key theme in the behavioural management literature. Challenging behaviour can be used to manipulate and split staff, to the detriment of teamwork. Hence adherence to an explicit, shared and constantly operationalised value base and ethos, reinforced thorough leadership and training, is essential. Poor inter-staff relationships and an inability to exercise and model successful conflict resolution between themselves is also a key factor in incident levels (Maier, 1999).

Legally valid as a last-resort risk prevention response only, restraint should not be employed to coerce compliance. In the absence of legitimate corporal punishment, a debate on the basis of staff control is essential. Control is in many ways illusory. It is conceded not demanded. Where effective control is exercised it is through the medium of relationships and the giving and withdrawing of the approval of a person (i.e. staff) significant to the service user. As Millham *et al.* (1981) (cited in Social Work Services Inspectorate for Scotland, 1997) argue it is the 'ethos' of the establishment which effectively controls:

> by fashioning a system of mutually held expectations, values and norms of conduct which exercise restraint on members. Control in a community home rests, as it does in a family, in demonstrating that within its walls a child receives more physical care, more love, understanding and encouragement than he is likely to experience outside.

Where service user behaviour presents a risk, care plans and individual risk assessment known to, and followed by, all staff are essential.

Resourcing

It is self-evident that without adequate resourcing challenges increase. Boredom through lack of stimulating activities may lead to confrontations. Staff may fear challenging service users, resulting in a disastrous reduction in positive interaction rates. Individual staff may be highly skilled, yet, in inadequately resourced agencies fire fighting and crisis management will erode their therapeutic impact. Although rigidity should be avoided, routines and timetabling give structure to daily experience and help (especially cognitively impaired service users) to manage anxiety through prediction of events and the management of transitions.

Training

The current emphasis on reactive crisis management training using the 'train and pray approach' is often used as a replacement for, rather than as an adjunct to, properly designed and individualised training strategies, which also induct staff into the values, aims and practices of the agency. Training is not, however, a panacea, and is often the focus of highly unrealistic expectations. Staff knowledge should be appraised and a clear expectation should operate that staff will be required to discus knowledge gained in regular supervision sessions and to demonstrate learning in daily practice. The creation of 'reflective practitioners' is an essential goal.

Data

Information on behavioural incidents may take many forms. Where services support users predisposed to patterns of challenging behaviour, functional analysis (Durand and Crimmons, 1988) can be used to identify likely setting conditions and triggers and to devise appropriate team responses. Information on the use of restrictive measures can be used to chart individual behaviours and needs, but it also acts as a performance indicator to assess the utility of agency approaches. However, all initiatives founder on the rock of service culture. Incident under-reporting is endemic, often fed by the belief that stigma and punishment will result for individuals involved in critical incidents. Demonstrable support, in the form of post-incident debriefing and agency responses which value staff, is a lynch pin of accurate data gathering. Where reporting procedures are viewed by staff as a purely administrative box-ticking exercise, the probability of reduced morale, under-reporting and non-approved responses is increased.

Debriefing

The systematic and supportive exploration of a critical or sentinel event is essential from a range of perspectives:

■ to support staff
■ to promote individual staff learning
■ to reduce staff trauma
■ to promote insight and learning for the aggressor
■ to restore relationships
■ to audit and address the adequacy of agency crisis management arrangements
■ to close the feedback loop by reviewing policies, procedures, individual risk assessments, care plans and staff training needs analysis in the light of debriefing conclusions

However, debriefing must be undertaken as a routine and skilled process, supported by agency policy, with a clear rationale which distinguishes between the controversial critical incident stress debriefing model (Mitchell and Everly, 1993) and the required managerial debriefing model (Paterson and Leadbetter, 1999; Richards, 2003).

Leadership

Management is making people do what you want them to do.
Leadership is making people want to do what you want them to do.

Rather than Rome, the preceding agenda leads all roads to the issue of leadership. Many managers are undoubtedly efficient administrators. It is, however, necessary to distinguish between managerialism and leadership. Many do things right. But do they do the right thing?

Managers	Leaders
Administrate	Innovate
Focus on systems and structures	Focus on people
Rely on control	Inspire trust
Have a short-range view	Have a long-term view
Have eyes on the bottom line	Have eyes on the horizon
Initiate	Originate
Accept the status quo	Challenge the status quo
Do things right	Do the right things

The absence of an explicit conceptual practice framework, identified by successive national reports, places the responsibility on service leaders to offer a clear vision and practice model, promoted and reinforced through policy, procedures and personal modelling.

In the authors' experience one manifestation of the 'reductionist' perspective is the habitual absence of senior managers from national conferences on restraint reduction, management workshops on challenging behaviour and training events. For instance, an innovative Scottish Government sponsored national conference explicitly aimed at chief executive officers and service directors on the issue of restraint attracted a total of one senior manager. This is arguably less a result of the undoubted time pressure on senior staff than the belief that behavioural management is a tactical staff skill agenda rather than a strategic agency issue.

Leadership takes many forms. It must however:

- be shared at many levels
- explicitly articulate the service vision
- lead from the front – model the skills and walk the talk
- take time for its own development
- be consultative and inclusive
- be decisive
- be visible

Conclusion

We are at a societal crossroads. The cat is out of the bag and the clock is running on the widespread use of restrictive practices to control challenging behaviour in human services. Competing frames locate the problem and solution at the level of the individual versus the organisation. The evidence is, however, unequivocal, regardless of the origins of challenging behaviour: services can be designed to ensure both safety and therapeutic management of aggressive behaviour. Reductions of both aggressive behaviour and restraint are predominantly effected by organisational effectiveness, rather than individual pathology. A paradigm shift is therefore crucial. A growing body of case examples demonstrate that significant restraint reduction is possible.

The fundamental question on restraint eradication, however, is – do we want to? Or will the use of coercive measures continue to be used to mask service deficiencies and a lack of leadership at agency and Governmental levels?

References

Allen, D. (2000a) *Training Carers in Physical Interventions: Towards Evidence Based Practice*. British Institute of Learning Disabilities, Kidderminster.

Allen, D. (2000b) Recent research on physical aggression in persons with intellectual disability: an overview. *Journal of Intellectual and Developmental Disability*, **25**(1), 41–57.

Allen, D. (ed.) (2003) *Behaviour Management in Intellectual Disabilities: Ethical Responses to Challenging Behaviour*. British Institute of Learning Disabilities, Kidderminster.

Allan, B. (1998) *Holding Back. Restraint Rarely and Safely*. Lucky Duck Publishing, Bristol.

Argyris, C. and Schön, D. (1978) *Organisational Learning: a Theory of Action Perspective*. Reading, MA.

Baker, P. A. and Bissmire, D. (2000). A pilot study of the use of physical intervention in the crisis management of people with intellectual disability who present challenging behaviour. *Journal of Applied Research in Intellectual Disabilities*, **13**(1), 38–45.

Baker, P. and Allen, D. (2001) Physical abuse and physical interventions in learning disabilities: an element of risk? *Journal of Adult Protection*, **3**(2), 25–31.

BBC (1999) *McIntyre Under Cover – One Man, Four Lives*. BBC, London.

Bell, L. and Stark, C. (1998) *Measuring Competence in Physical Restraint Skills in Residential Child Care*. Scottish Office Central Research Unit, Edinburgh.

Bloom, S. (1997) *Creating Sanctuary: Toward an Evolution of Sane Societies*. Routledge, New York.

Bloom, S. (2006) *Organisational Stress as a Barrier to Trauma – Sensitive Change and System Transformation*. Adapted from *Living Sanctuary; Complex Antidotes to Organisational Stress in a Changing World*, http://www.santuarynet.com/.

Birleson, P. (1999) Turning child and adolescent mental-health services into learning organizations. *Clinical Child Psychology and Psychiatry*, **4**(2), 265–74.

Bleetman, A. and Boatman, P. (2001) *An Overview of Control and Restraint Issues for the Health Service*. Department of Health, London.

Braverman, M. (1999) *Preventing Workplace Violence. A Guide for Employers and Practitioners*. Sage Publications, London.

British Institute for Learning Disabilities (BILD) (2006) *Code of Practice for the Use of Physical Interventions*, 2nd edn. BILD, Kidderminster.

Bowie, V. (2006) Organizational management and culture as key triggers of workplace violence. Paper presented at Reaching for the Light, International Research Symposium. University of Stirling, Stirling.

Bowers, L., Nijman, H., Allan, T., Simpson, A., Warren, J. and Turner, L. (2006) Prevention and management of aggression training and violent incidents in UK acute psychiatric wards. *Psychiatric Services*, **57**(7), 1022–6.

Bullard, L., Fulmore, D. and Johnstone, K. (2003) *Reducing the Use of Restraint and Seclusion: Promising Practices and Successful Strategies*. Child Welfare League of America Press, Washington, DC.

CAICA – Coalition Against Institutionalised Child Abuse. http://www.caica.org/ (accessed 29 October 2008).

CALM Annual Audit Reports 2001–2007. Available to user organisations and academic researchers from CALM Training Services, Menstrie.

Carr, E. G., Horner, R. H. and Turnbull, A.P. (1999) *Positive Behavioural Support for People with Developmental Disabilities. A Research Synthesis*. American Association on Mental Retardation, Washington, DC.

Carlile of Berriew, Lord (2006) *An Independent Inquiry Into the Use of Physical Restraint, Solitary Confinement and Forcible Strip Searching of Children in Prisons, Secure Training Centres and Local Authority Secure Children's Homes*. Howard League for Penal Reform, London.

Child Welfare League of America (CWLA) (2004) *Achieving Better Outcomes for Children & Families – Reducing Restraint and Seclusion*. CWLA, Washington, DC.

Colton, D. (2004) *Checklist for Assessing Your Organization's Readiness for Reducing Seclusion and Restraint*. Commonwealth Center for Children and Adolescence, Staunton, VA.

Davis, P. (2004) *Mental Health Nursing Journal*, May.

Department of Health/Department for Education and Skills (2002) *Guidance on the Use of Physical Interventions for Staff Working with Children and Adults who Display Extreme Behaviour in Association with Learning Disability and/or Autism Spectrum Disorders*. Department of Health/Department for Education and Skills, London.

Deveau, R. and McGill, P. (2007) *As the Last Resort: Reducing the Use of Restrictive Physical Interventions*. Tizard Centre, Canterbury.

Duff, L., Gray, R. and Bristow, F. (1996) The use of control and restraint techniques in acute psychiatric units. *Psychiatric Care*, **3**(6), 230–4.

Durand, V. M. and Crimmons, D. B. (1988) Identifying the variables, maintaining self injurious behaviour, *Journal of Autism and Developmental Disorders*, **18**(1), 99–117.

Emerson, E. (2003) The prevalence of psychiatric disorders in children and adolescents with and without intellectual disabilities. *Journal of Intellectual Disability Research*, **47**(1), 51–8.

Emerson, E. and Hatton, C. (2000) *Violence Against Social Care Workers Supporting People with Learning Difficulties: A Review*. University of Lancaster, Lancaster.

European Court of Human Rights (1995) *Ribitsch v Austria* (A/336), 4 December.

General Accounting Office (GAO) (of the United States) (1999) *Report to Congressional Requesters: Mental Health: Improper Restraint or Seclusion Places People at Risk*. GAO, Washington, DC.

Harris, J. (1993) The nature and extent of aggressive behaviour among people with learning difficulties (mental handicap) in a single health district. *Journal of Intellectual Disability Research*, **37**(3), 221–42.

Hart, D. (2008) *Restrictive Physical Intervention in Secure Children's Homes*. National Children's Bureau Department for Children, Schools and Families, London.

Healthcare Commission and Commission for Social Care Inspection (2006) *Joint Investigation into the Provision of Services for People with Learning Disabilities at Cornwall Partnership NHS Trust*. Healthcare Commission, London.

Healthcare Commission (2007) *Investigation into the Service for People with Learning Disabilities Provided by Sutton and Merton Primary Care Trust*. Healthcare Commission, London.

Holdon, M. and Curry, D. (2008) Learning from the research. In: *For Our Own Safety: Examining the Safety of High-risk Interventions for Children and Young People* (eds. M. A. Nunno, L. B. Bullard and D. M. Day). Child Welfare League of America, Washington, DC.

Hucksthorn, K. (2005) *Six Core Strategies for Reducing Seclusion and Restraint Use*. National Technical Assistance Center, Virginia.

Joint Commission for Health Care (2005) *Root Cause Analysis in Health Care: Tools And Techniques*. Joint Commission for Health Care, Washington, DC.

Johnstone, S. (1988) Guidelines for social workers coping with violent clients. *British Journal of Social Work*, **18**(4), 377–90.

Koegel, L. (ed.) (1996) *Positive Behavioral Support: Including People with Difficult Behavior in the Community*. Brookes, Baltimore.

Leadbetter, D. (1994) Need for care over methods of restraint. *Community Care*, 18–24 August, p. 13.

Leadbetter, D. (2003) Good practice in physical interventions. In: *Behaviour Management in Intellectual Disabilities: Ethical Responses to Challenging Behaviour*, 2nd edn (ed. D. Allen). British Institute of Learning Disabilities, Kidderminster.

Leadbetter , D. (2007) Millfields Charter, finding the middle ground. *Learning Disability Practice*, **10**(3), 34–7.

Leadbetter (2008) Restraint reduction. In: *Behaviour Management in Intellectual Disabilities: Ethical Responses to Challenging Behaviour*, 2nd edn (ed. D. Allen). British Institute of Learning Disabilities, Kidderminster.

Leadbetter (2009) Restraint reduction. In: *Behaviour Management in Intellectual Disabilities: Ethical Responses to Challenging Behaviour* (ed. D. Allen), 2nd edn. British Institute of Learning Disabilities, Kidderminster.

Leadbetter, D. and Paterson, B. (1996) Pressing need for physical restraint evaluation. *Professional Social Work*, February, p. 5.

Lee, S., Wright,. S., Sayer, J., Parr, A., Gray, R. and Gournay, K. (2001) Physical restraint training for nurses in English and Welsh psychiatric intensive care and regional secure units. *Journal of Mental Health*, **10**(2), 151–62.

Maier, G. J. (1999) Psychological issues in treatment: transference and counter transference. In: *Medical Management of the Violent Patient: Clinical Assessment and Therapy* (ed. K. Tardiff). Dekker, New York.

Martin, A., McDonnell, A., Paterson, B. and Leadbetter, D. (2008) Developing a tool to evaluate the risks associated with using physical interventions – report of project undertaken by BILD. In: *Behaviour Management in Intellectual Disabilities: Ethical Responses to Challenging Behaviour*, 2nd edn (ed. D. Allen). British Institute of Learning Disabilities, Kidderminster.

McDonnell, A. (2007) Millfields Charter – why I am in favour. *Learning Disability Practice*, **10**(3), 26–9.

McDonnell, A., Sturmey, P. and Butt, S. (2005) *Training in Physical Interventions; A Review of the Literature*. Unpublished report. Available from Studio 111 Training.

McDonnell, A., Paterson, B., Leadbetter, D. and Martin, A. (2008) *Physical Intervention Risk Assessment Tool – Safe, Teachable, Effective, Acceptable, Retained – STEAR Tool*. http://www.bild.org/ (accessed 29 October 2008).

Mitchell, J. T. and Everly, G. S. (1993) *Critical Incident Stress Debriefing*. Chevron, Ellicot.

Mohr, W. K., Mahon, M. M. and Noone, M. J. (1998) A restraint on restraint: the need to reconsider the use of restrictive interventions. *Archive of Psychiatric Nursing*, **12**(2), 95–106.

Meichenbaum, D. (1977) *Cognitive Behavioural Modification*. Plenum Press, New York.

Mental Health Act Commission (2005) *Count Me In: the National Mental Health and Ethnicity Census*. Mental Health Act Commission, Nottingham.

Morgan, R. (2004) *Children's Views on Restraint. The Views of Children and Young People in Residential Homes and Residential Special Schools*. Newcastle, Office of the Children's Rights Director.

Morrison, L., Duryea, P. B., Moore, C. and Nathanson-Shinn, A. (2002) *The Lethal Hazard of Prone Restraint – Positional Asphyxia*. Protection & Advocacy Inc., Publication No. 7018.01, Los Angeles.

Murphy, G., Kelly-Pike, A., McGill, P., Jones, S. and Byatt, J. (2003) Physical interventions with people with intellectual disabilities; staff training and policy frameworks. *Journal of Applied Research in Intellectual Disabilities*, **16**(2), 115–25.

National Association of State Mental Health Program Directors (1999) *Position Statement on Seclusion and Restraint*. National Technical Assistance Center for State Mental Health Planning, Alexandria, VA.

Novaco, R. W. (1975) *Anger Control: the Development and Evaluation of an Experimental Treatment*. DC Health, Lexington, MA.

Nunno, M. A., Bullard, L. B. and Day, D. M. (eds.) (2008) *For Our Own Safety: Examining the Safety of High-risk Interventions for Children and Young People*. Child Welfare League of America, Washington, DC.

O'Neill, R. E., Horner, R. H. and Albin, R. W. (1997) *Functional Assessment of Programme Development for Problem Behaviour. A Practical Handbook.* Brooks/Cole, Pacific Grove, CA.

Paterson, B., Leadbetter, D. and Bowie, V. (1999) Supporting staff exposed to violence at work: the role of psychological debriefing. *International Journal of Nursing Studies,* **36**(6), 479–86.

Paterson, B., Bradley, P., Stark, C., Saddler, D., Leadbetter, D. and Allen, D. (2003) Deaths associated with restraint use in health and social care in the United Kingdom. The results of a preliminary survey. *Journal of Psychiatric and Mental Health Nursing,* **10**(1), 3–15.

Paterson, B. (2007) Millfields Charter, drawing the wrong conclusions, *Learning Disability Practice,* **10**(3), 30–3.

Paterson, B. and Duxbury, J. (2007) Restraint and the question of validity. *Nursing Ethics,* **14**(4), 535–45.

Paterson, B., Leadbetter, D., Crichton, J. and Miller, G. (2008) Adopting a public health model to reduce violence and restraints in children's residential care facilities. In: *For Our Own Safety: Examining the Safety of High-risk Interventions for Children and Young People* (eds. M. A. Nunno, L. B. Bullard and D. M. Day). Child Welfare League of America Press, Washington, DC.

Paterson, B. and Miller, G. (2006) *Promoting Safe and Therapeutic Services, National Health Service Security Management Service, Trainers Handbook.* Counter Fraud & Security Management Services, London.

Paterson, B., Miller, G., Leadbetter, D. and Bowie, V. (2008) Zero tolerance and violence in services for people with mental health needs. *Mental Health Practice,* **11**(8), 30–3.

Perkins, J. and Leadbetter, D. (2002) An evaluation of aggression management training in a special educational setting. *Emotional and Behavioural Difficulties,* **7**(1), 19–34.

Pitman, J. (1994) Papers of the Society for Improving the Conditions of the Insane. *Proceedings of the Royal College of Physicians Edinburgh,* **24**, 420–7.

Richards, J. (2003) *Management of Workplace Violence Victims. International Labour Office ILO International Council of Nurses ICN World Health Organisation.* WHO Public Services International PSI, Geneva.

Royal College of Psychiatrists (RCP) (1998) *The Management of Violence in Clinical Settings: An Evidence Based Guideline.* Gaskell, London.

Royal College of Psychiatrists (RCP) (2005) *Managing Imminent Violence in Learning Disability Settings.* RCP, London.

Royal College of Psychiatrists (RCP) (2008) *Challenging Behaviour: a Unified Approach. Clinical and Service Guidelines for Supporting People with Learning Disabilities Who Are at Risk of Receiving Abusive or Restrictive Practices.* RCP, London.

Sailas, E. and Fenton, M. (2000) Seclusion and restraint for people with serious mental illnesses. *Cochrane Database of Systematic Reviews,* **1**.

Sethi, D., Marais, S., Seedat, M., Nurse, J. and Butchart, A. (2004) *Handbook for the Documentation of Interpersonal Violence Prevention Programmes.* Department of Injuries and Violence Prevention, World Health Organization, Geneva.

Sequeira, H. and Halstead, S. (2001) 'Is it meant to hurt, is it? Management of violence in women with developmental disabilities. *Violence Against Women*, **7**(4), 462–76.

Sequeira, H. and Halstead, S. (2004) Psychological effects on nursing staff of administering physical restraint in a secure psychiatric hospital: 'when I go home, its then I think about it'. *Journal of Forensic Practice*, **6**(3), 3–15.

Smallridge, P. and Williamson, A. (2008) *Independent Review of Restraint in Juvenile Secure Settings*. Ministry of Justice/Department for Children Schools and Families, London.

Stubbs, B., Leadbetter, D., Paterson, B., Yorston, G. and Knight, C. (2009) Physical Interventions in the management of aggression and violent behaviour: reflecting on the impact of training and patient views on the procedure. *Journal of Psychiatric and Mental Health Nursing Physical Interventions*, **16**(1), 99–105.

Social Care Institute for Excellence (2008) *Working with Challenging and Disruptive Situations in Residential Child Care: Sharing Effective Practice*. Social Care Institute for Excellence, London.

Social Work Services Inspectorate for Scotland (1997) *Children's Safeguards Review (The Kent Report)*. Social Work Services Inspectorate for Scotland, Edinburgh.

Titus, R. (1989) Therapeutic crisis intervention training at Kinark child and family services: assessing its impact. *Journal of Child and Youth Care*, **4**(3), 461–71.

Tucker, R. (2004) NMC national conference on violence. Some nurses too quick to restrain patients. Press statement, 21 August. http://www.nmcuk.org/nmc/main-pressStatements/Somenursestooquicktorestrainpatients (accessed 29 October 2008).

Waclawski, E., Bell, L. and Leyden, J. (2004) Impact of training in the management of aggression on the incident rates and perceptions of staff. *Occupational and Environmental Medicine*, **61**(11), 20.

Wardhaugh, J. and Wilding, P. (1993) Towards an explanation of the corruption of care. *Critical Social Care*, **37**(13), 4–31.

Weiss, E. M. (1998) Deadly restraint. *Hartford Courant*, 11–15 October.

Zarola, A. and Leather, P. (2006) *Violence and Aggression Management for Trainers and Managers: a National Evaluation of the Training Provision in Health Care Settings. Report to the Health and Safety Executive*. Research Report 440. University of Nottingham for the Health and Safety Executive, Nottingham.

Index